VOICES IN THE SKY

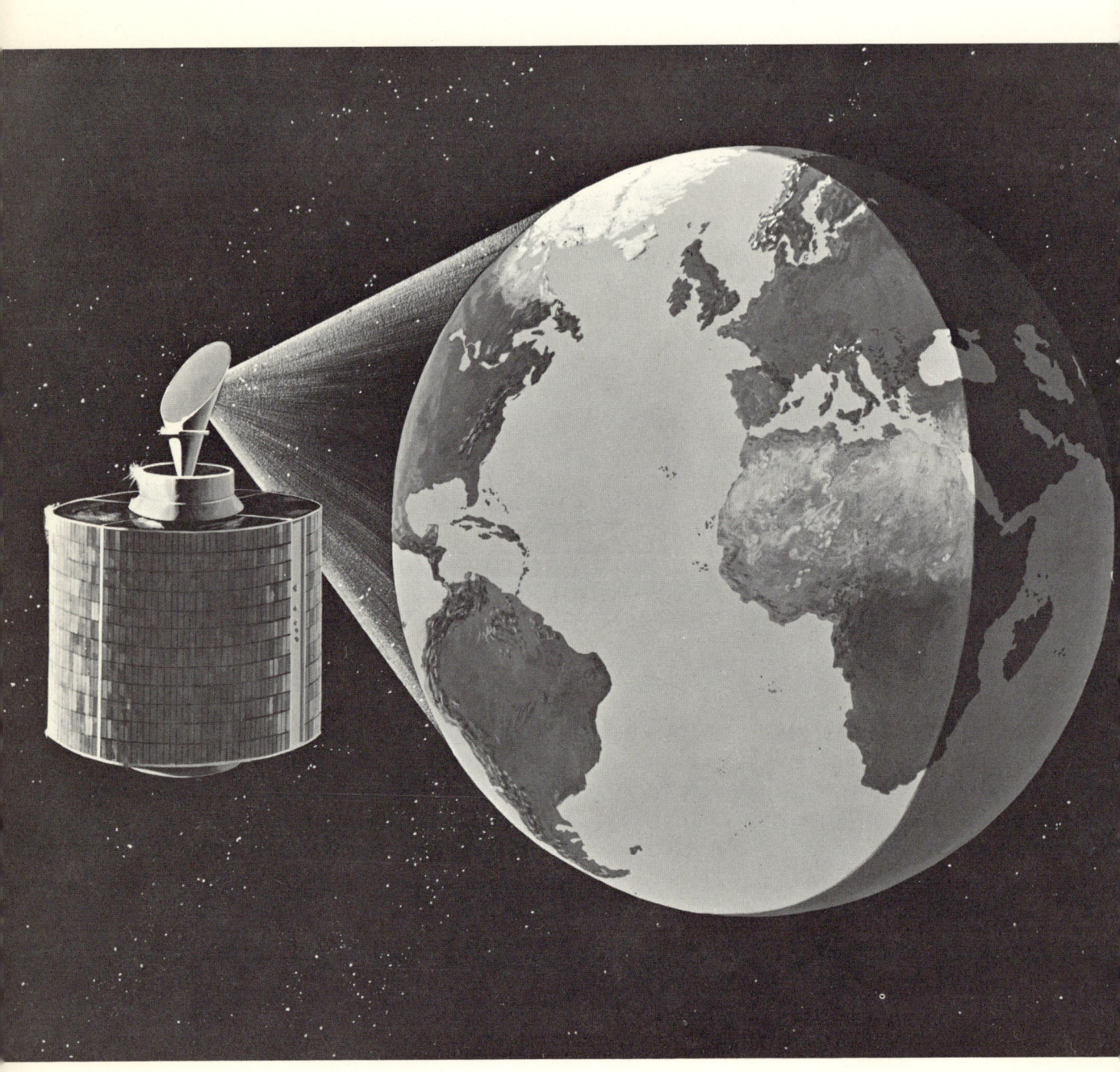

VOICES IN THE SKY
The Story of Communications Satellites

By Don Dwiggins
Illustrated with Photographs and Diagrams

232411

GOLDEN GATE JUNIOR BOOKS
SAN CARLOS, CALIFORNIA

To TONI and CHUCK

Copyright © 1969 by Don Dwiggins
All rights reserved
Library of Congress Catalog card number 69-15400
Lithographed in the United States of America
by Anderson, Ritchie & Simon, Los Angeles

CONTENTS

VOICES IN THE SKY 9
    How Communications Satellites Work

THE BEGINNINGS 14
    A Dream of Global Communications

SCORE—THE TALKING MISSILE 19
    World's First Communications Satellite

LOW-ALTITUDE SATELLITES 24
    Satellites That Carry Messages

SYNCOMS—THE FIRST SYNCHRONOUS SATELLITES 35
    Man Hangs Out a New Star

COMMERCIAL SATELLITES ARRIVE 44
    Orbiting Telephone Exchanges

RUSSIAN LIGHTNING IN THE SKY 57
    World's First Domestic Satellite Network

MILITARY COMMUNICATIONS SATELLITES 63
    Patrolling Worldwide Battlefronts

Chronology 76

Glossary 77

Index 79

Frontispiece and cover: Intelsat III, global satellite.

FOREWORD

During the period of ten years which has passed since the surprise launch of SCORE, the world's first communications satellite, giant strides have been taken in the evolution of operational satellite systems. As chronicled in this book, the forty-odd communications satellites now in orbit interconnect embryonic commercial and military networks. These satellites are being used both internationally and domestically for a wide variety of transmissions — telephony, television, telegraphy, facsimile — fulfilling most goals of their developers. The present status of communications satellites might properly be termed the end of the beginning.

What will be achieved in the decade of the 1970's? The large capacity satellites now under development will be put into service, effecting a substantial reduction in the cost of international communications. Transoceanic telephone will become commonplace for both business and pleasure calls, while the television capacity available will permit some international conferences to be accomplished by telecommunications rather than by transportation of the participants. Domestic and regional communications satellite systems will be introduced in a number of areas. The United States, Canada, Mexico, Brazil, Japan, Australia, and Western Europe will operate general-purpose satellite systems which will complement their surface communications, increasing the coverage and capacity and providing alternate routing during outages of the surface systems caused by hurricanes and earthquakes.

The communications satellite mission of greatest significance remaining to be accomplished, in the opinion of many, is that of educational television broadcasting. There is a worldwide need for lowering the costs and increasing the scope and reach of education, particularly in the developing nations, and satellite systems for the distribution of television have been shown to have technical and economic advantages over surface distribution systems. Furthermore, they can be implemented much sooner. The main obstacle to the development of such systems is not the fear of failure, but the fear of success and the political problems which may be encountered in their use, or misuse. I feel strongly that these risks are worth taking, for a satellite system for mass education could make a substantial contribution to the enlightenment of the human race.

In this book Don Dwiggins relates the exciting story of the development of communications satellites. *Voices In The Sky* is a highly readable account of an important era in the history of man's technological progress, and it forms a foundation for a better understanding of the advancements to come.

December, 1968   HAROLD A. ROSEN
                 Manager, Satellites Systems Laboratories
                 Hughes Aircraft Company

AUTHOR'S PREFACE

THE WORLD TODAY is at a crossroads, one in which man stands a fair chance of controlling his own destiny. Depending on the path he chooses to follow, his future will be bright and harmonious or dark with despair. Our fantastic twentieth-century technology has given mankind awesome power which he must learn to control and direct before drawing fully upon it to serve his needs.

Nuclear energy, supersonic flight, long-range weather prediction are only a few of today's technological marvels which man is learning to use as modern tools with which to fashion his future. In an effort to bring the world closer together in a meaningful way, the late President John F. Kennedy, at the opening of this decade, dedicated the nation to achieving global communications through our new-found space technology.

Now that this achievement is at hand, we must decide to utilize this great new tool for learning for the betterment of all mankind. In the words of John M. Mason, an early American theologian, "The aim of education should be to convert the mind into a living fountain, and not a reservoir. That which is filled by merely pumping in, will be emptied by pumping out." It is for the youth of America to insure that, with this legacy, our "fountain of life" continues to flow freely.

DON DWIGGINS

ACKNOWLEDGEMENTS

THE AUTHOR IS indebted to many friends in government and industry who assisted in the compilation of material on which this work, *Voices In The Sky,* is based. To list them all would be impracticable; however, my individual thanks go to each one who contributed a part of the whole story of Space Age communications.

In particular, the personnel and information officers of the following organizations were of invaluable help: National Aeronautics and Space Administration; United Nations; Department of Defense; Air Force Space & Missile Systems Organization (SAMSO); United States Navy; USAF/IO Hollywood; Air Force National Range Division; Communications Satellite Corporation; Ford-Philco WDL Division; Hughes Aircraft Company; TRW Systems Group; Radio Corporation of America; American Telephone & Telegraph Company; McDonnell Douglas Aircraft Company; American Broadcasting Company; Tass News Agency; M.I.T. Lincoln Laboratory.

VOICES IN THE SKY

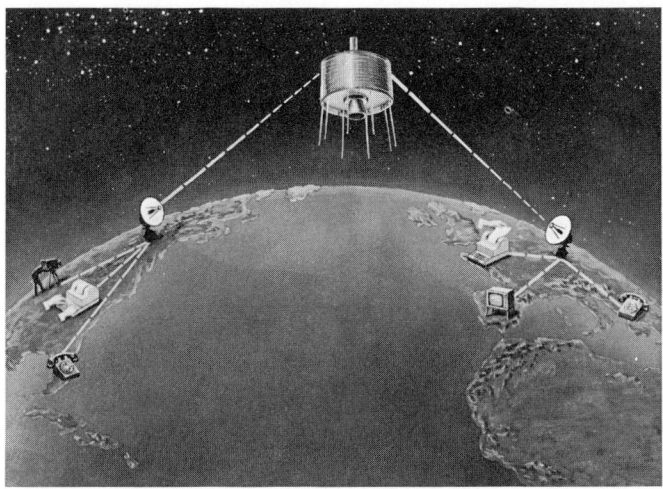

Satellites that carry telephone, facsimile, television transmissions.

IN THIS SECOND decade of the Space Age, mankind already is reaping the harvest of ten years of toil and is conquering our last frontier—the sky—for the peaceful use of all nations. Our space explorers have reached to the moon, and beyond. Weather satellites bring us instant warnings of approaching storms. Orbiting observatories let us peer to the far limits of our universe.

Today, many different kinds of orbiting satellites now bring us new knowledge for making a better world to live in. Foremost among these are the communications satellites. These unique orbiting space stations, weighing from a mere one hundred pounds to more than a ton, are virtual flying switchboards which bring us voices from the sky, relay stations speeding at more than 17,000 miles per hour through looping celestial journeys.

Soon the growing network of ground stations will link all nations of the globe on one vast party line; any two people on earth will be able to converse, no matter where they are.

Former President Lyndon B. Johnson, on August 14, 1967, told Congress in a message on Communications Policy: "A telephone call from Rangoon to Djakarta must still go through Tokyo... A call from

American Samoa to Tahiti goes by way of Oakland, California... Such an archaic system of international communications is no longer necessary. The communications satellite knows no geographic boundary, is dependent on no cable, owes allegiance to no single language or political philosophy. Man now has it within his power to speak directly to his fellow man in all nations."

Until the first transatlantic telephone cable was completed in 1956, there was no reliable means of voice communications across oceans. True, Marconi in the 1920's was able to send wavering voice messages over 2,400 miles, by bouncing shortwave radio signals off an ionized reflecting layer some kilometers above the ground. Because shortwaves

Microwaves travel in straight lines.

travel long distances in this manner, they are subject to atmospheric disturbances, particularly during magnetic storms from the sun. At mid-twentieth century 95 percent of all long distance radio communications was still conducted with shortwave transmissions by means of reflection from the ionosphere.

Yet, by the 1950's *microwaves* were recognized as being ideal for transmission of voice, facsimile, teletype and television traffic, their short, ultrahigh frequency virtually immune to interference. Because microwaves travel in a straight line and do not reflect from the iono-

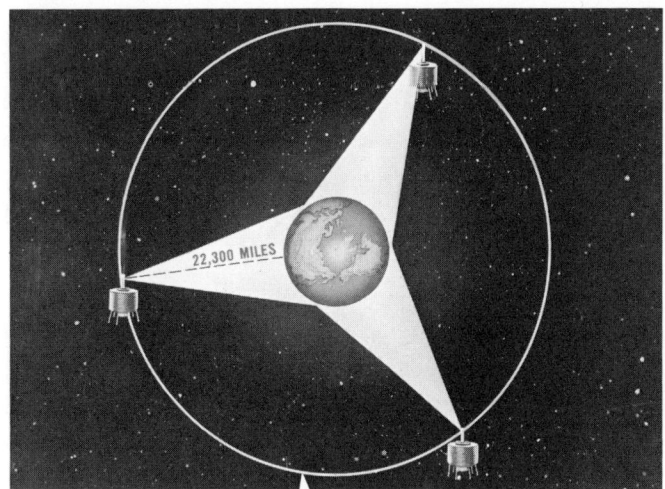

Three synchronous satellites cover the world. Traveling 6,000 miles per hour in a 22,300-mile orbit, they appear to be stationary overhead.

sphere, our transcontinental microwave system employs relay towers spaced at approximately 30-mile line-of-sight intervals across the country.

To communicate across oceans by microwave without satellites would require a string of relay stations floating on vessels 30 miles apart, or one huge tower 475 miles high in mid-Atlantic! Obviously, orbiting satellites are the simple answer to relaying microwaves from one continent to another.

There are two types of communications satellites. An active (repeater) satellite is a complex electronic device able to receive signals from earth-

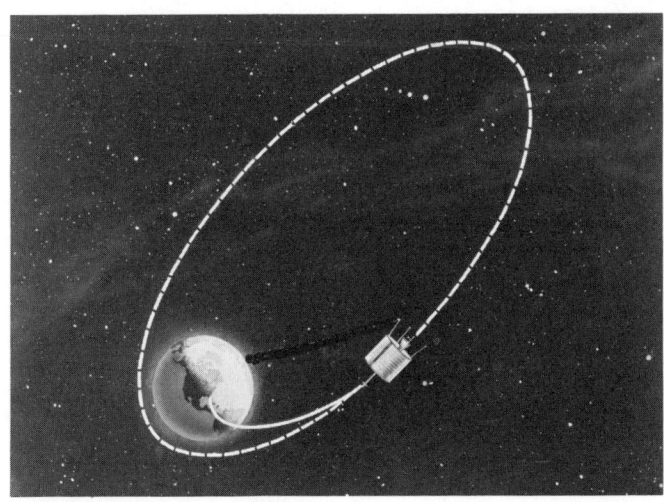

How satellites achieve an elliptical orbit. Russia's Molniya satellites use elliptical orbits to cover far-northern latitudes.

based ground station transmitters, amplifying those signals and relaying them back down to other ground stations. Passive (reflector) satellites, which do not amplify signals, need very powerful ground transmitters and highly sensitive receivers, but as they have no working parts they are more reliable than repeater satellites, whose lifetime is limited to the reliability of their internal circuitry.

A satellite's orbit has much to do with its ability to serve as a microwave relay station. Low-orbit satellites may cross the sky from horizon to horizon in a matter of minutes, and thus are useable for real-time (instantaneous broadcast) relay only when visible to both transmitter and receiver stations. Other low-orbit satellites can store messages on magnetic tape, to relay them later on when triggered by another earth station. These are called courier satellites.

Another kind of satellite orbit is called the *synchronous* orbit. At an altitude of approximately 22,300 miles above the earth's surface, a satellite traveling at 6,000 miles per hour will complete its circular orbital path in about 24 hours (exactly 23 hours 56 minutes), the time it takes the earth to turn during one day. Thus, a synchronous satellite appears to hang motionless in the sky. At such a distance, virtually an entire hemisphere can be "illuminated" (seen) by a synchronous satellite, and earth stations need only to aim their antennas at a single point, rather than follow a moving satellite across the sky.

Such synchronous positioning is possible only in the equatorial plane, if the satellite is to remain apparently motionless. Three such satellites spaced 120 degrees apart can completely cover the globe with line-of-sight microwave coverage.

Another satellite orbit is the *elliptical* orbit, in which the "bird" comes within a few hundred miles of earth at its perigee (low point), then swings outward for thousands of miles at apogee (high point). Such an orbit is used to advantage by Russian *Molniya* satellites. At an apogee of 40,000 kilometers (25,000 miles) above the Northern Hemisphere, Molniya 1 can illuminate the entire U.S.S.R., including such remote areas as the Magadan District, the Kamchatka Peninsula, Sakhalin Island and Yakutsk. (An earth station in the Far North would have to point its antenna low to the horizon to lock onto a synchronous satellite above the equator, thus picking up critical ground interference).

One elliptical orbital system is the medium altitude *random* type, in which from 18 to 24 satellites orbit the earth (from 6,000 to 8,000 miles altitude), so that one or more would be visible at any one time. However, at certain times of the month such random satellites would

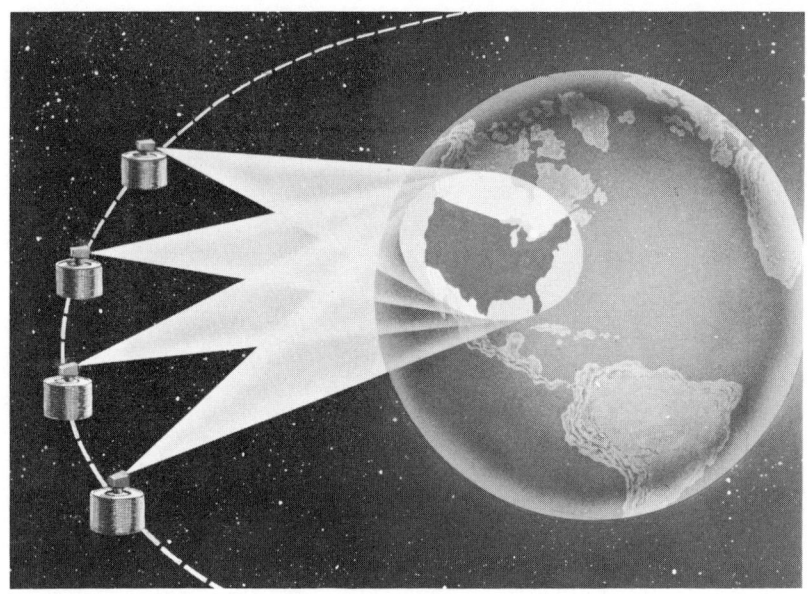

A domestic satellite system for the 1970's.

bunch together so that none would be commonly visible between two points of major interest, creating "blackouts."

Still another elliptical orbit is the medium altitude *phased* system in which a satellite necklace is strung around the globe, so arranged that, as one disappears below the horizon, another rises.

While most such systems today are global in nature and coverage, the U.S.S.R. was the first nation to establish a domestic communications satellite network, Orbita. When Russia entered the satellite era it was more economical for her to utilize the new space techniques than to build expensive land lines and microwave relay stations over the frozen tundra regions.

By contrast, the United States, with its well-developed transcontinental cable and microwave relay systems, could not very well afford to scrap such expensive installations in favor of satellites. Yet, a full-scale U. S. domestic satellite system in the early 1970's could consist of four high-capacity satellites operating with more than 150 earth stations. Such a system could provide 16 commercial TV channels, four educational TV channels, and 28,000 message channels. Even more advanced domestic systems are now planned for the late 1970's.

THE BEGINNINGS

ONE HUNDRED YEARS before the communications satellite era, born in 1958, with the launch of an amazing venture called Project SCORE, a group of leading American scientists, including Samuel F. B. Morse, inventor of the telegraph, and Cyrus Field, an industrialist, gathered in Ottawa, Canada, to celebrate completion of the first successful transatlantic submarine cable.

Until that day—August 17, 1858—the New and Old Worlds were separated not only by a vast ocean, but by a near-total lack of communications. It took twelve days for the fastest mail packets to reach New York from London; interchange of ideas between Europe and America was painfully slow.

Then came the historic first telegraph message over Cyrus Field's cable, twenty-five words from Queen Victoria to President James J. Buchanan.

Worldwide satellite-ground station net makes submarine cables obsolete.

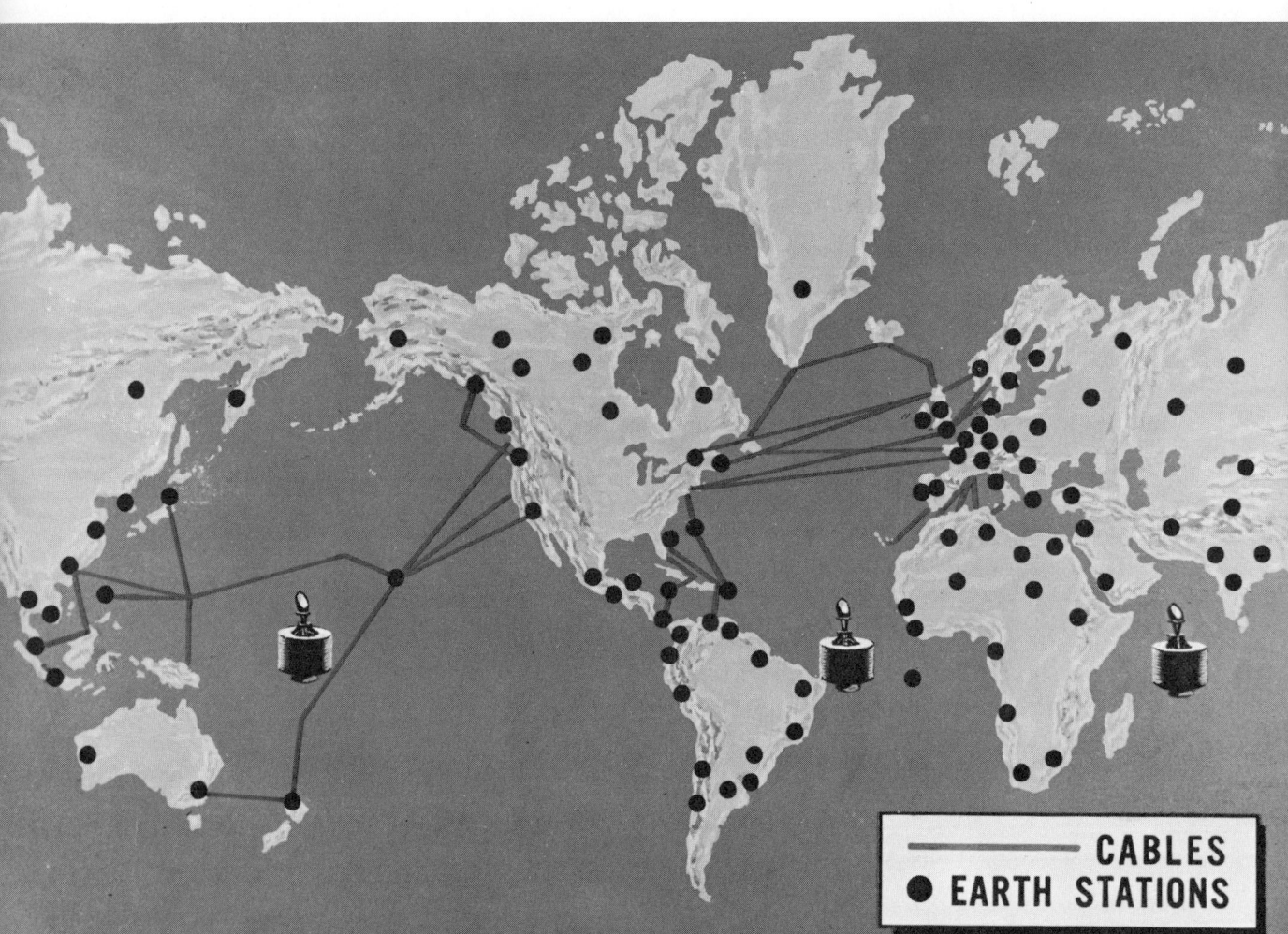

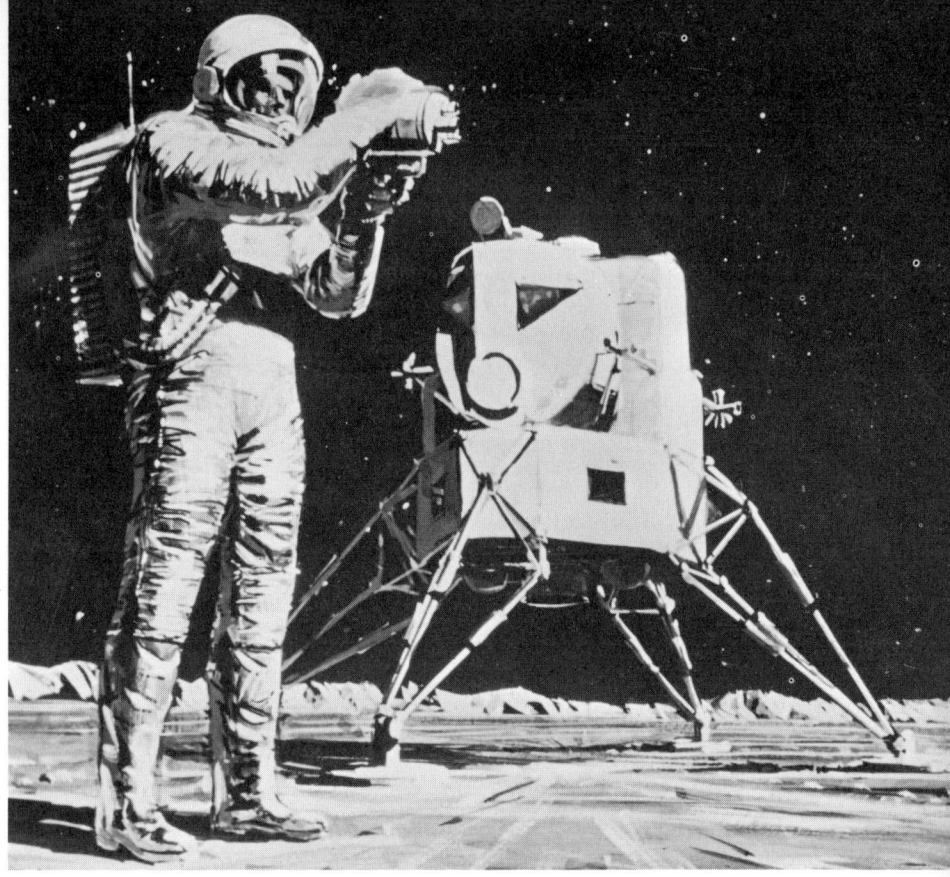

Project Apollo astronauts used communications satellite network to keep in touch with Mission Control Center.

England's former colonies were once more bound to her, this time by a wire 3,400 miles long. The message read:

"THE QUEEN DESIRES TO CONGRATULATE THE PRESIDENT UPON THE SUCCESSFUL COMPLETION OF THE GREAT INTERNATIONAL WORK, IN WHICH THE QUEEN HAS TAKEN THE GREATEST INTEREST."

Due to faulty insulation, Field's cable sputtered and died scarcely a month after its promising inaugural, and American scientists next turned to transocean ballooning projects to link the two worlds. The Civil War interrupted further development of all such communications schemes. When President Abraham Lincoln was assassinated on April 14, 1865, London did not know of it until twelve days later.

Field did get a transatlantic telegraph cable working in 1866, and in the next century three more would be added. The first transatlantic telephone cable brought high-quality voice communications between America and Europe only in 1956, two years before the first "talking satellite," SCORE, went up.

The trouble with cable transmissions was that a cable connected only two terminals, one at each end. Despite multiple channels in each cable, traffic was limited and rates were high—a one-way telephone cable link between New York and Paris cost $12,000 a month to lease. International television was out of the question.

Thus it was that a British science fiction writer, Arthur C. Clarke, in October, 1945, was considered something of a wild visionary when he published a prophetic description of things to come in the satellite field. Twelve years before Sputnik I opened the Space Age communications era, Clarke wrote, "It will be possible in a few more years to build radio controlled rockets which can be steered into orbits beyond the limits of the atmosphere and left to broadcast scientific information back to the earth. A little later, manned rockets will be able to make similar flights with sufficient excess power to break the orbit and return to earth."

One important orbit, Clarke noted, "has a radius of 42,000 kilometers and a period of exactly 24 hours. A body in such an orbit, if its plane coincided with that of the earth's equator, would revolve with the earth and would thus be stationary above the same spot on the planet. It would remain fixed in the sky of a whole hemisphere and unlike all other heavenly bodies would neither rise nor set."

It was Clarke's idea to send up parts of a space station by shuttle rocket and there assemble a manned active repeater communications station. "A transmission received from any point on earth," he predicted, "could be broadcast to the whole visible face of the globe, and thus the requirements of all possible (communications) services would be met."

Clarke worried about one possible stumbling block to his scheme—there was no direct evidence then at hand that radio waves from earth could penetrate the ionosphere. "Given sufficient transmitting power," he suggested, "we might obtain the necessary evidence by exploring for echoes from the moon."

He concluded that such a communications space station would permit "unrestricted use of a band at least 100,000 megacycles wide, and with the use of beams an almost unlimited number of channels would be available."

Clarke's thinking was sound, and it is a tribute to his brilliance that the course of technological history has followed his predictions closely. In fact, two months after his article on *Extra-Terrestrial Relays* appeared, the U. S. Army Signal Corps' Project Diana succeeded in bouncing radar signals off the moon and receiving them back on earth. With the moon serving as a passive communications satellite, voice messages were sent from Washington, D. C. to Hawaii over a distance of roughly half a million miles. Diana proved two things—that the ionosphere was

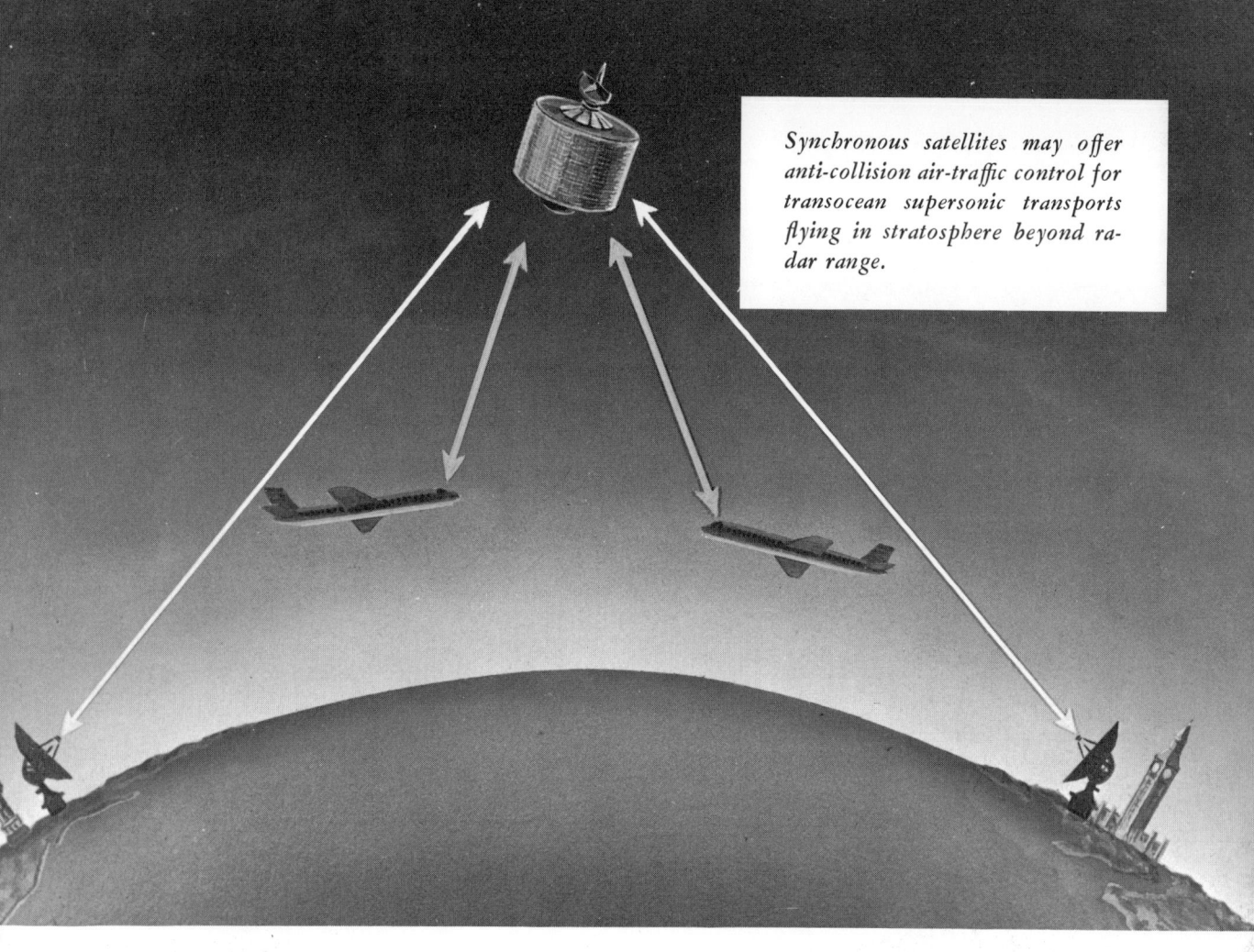

Synchronous satellites may offer anti-collision air-traffic control for transocean supersonic transports flying in stratosphere beyond radar range.

not an electronic barrier to radio communications with a satellite in synchronous orbit above it, and that radio signals could be sent over vast distances with relatively low power.

On May 2, 1946, only a few months after Diana, another independent research project concluded that technology had advanced to a point where it was feasible to design and build a satellite capable of being used as a communications relay station. This was the RAND Corporation's "Preliminary Design of an Experimental World-Circling Spaceship" which RAND felt should be built posthaste.

"To visualize the impact on the world," RAND prophesied, "one can imagine the consternation and admiration that would be felt here if the U. S. were to discover suddenly that some other nation had already put up a successful satellite! The nation which first makes significant achievements in space travel will be acknowledged as the world leader in both military and scientific techniques."

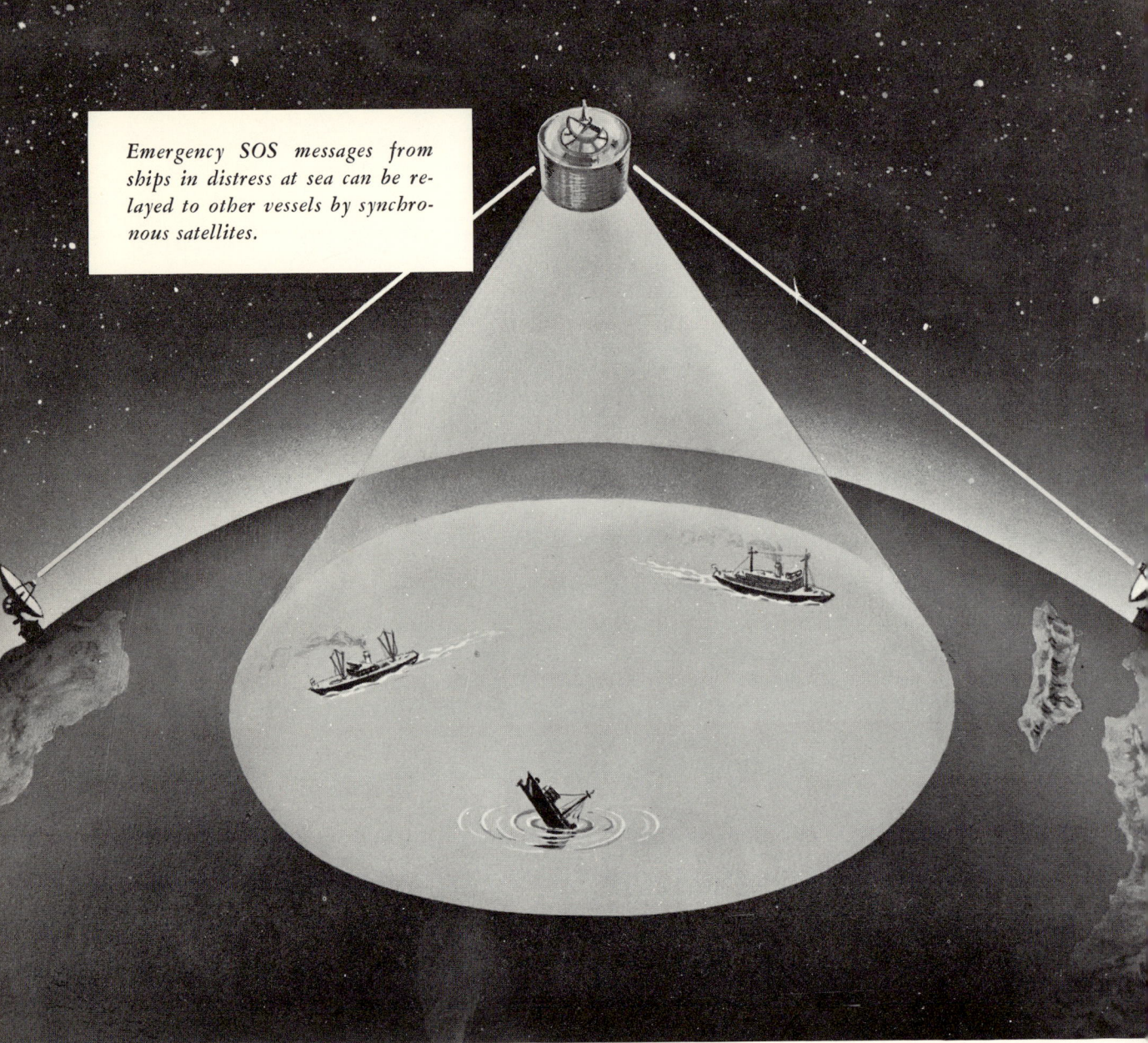

Emergency SOS messages from ships in distress at sea can be relayed to other vessels by synchronous satellites.

In ignoring this warning the United States did in fact suffer a loss of prestige to the U.S.S.R. when the Russian 184-pound Sputnik I successfully orbited on October 4, 1957, and transmitted its sing-song telemetry for twenty-one days before its orbit decayed. As a late starter in the Space Age, the United States nevertheless was determined to catch up with Russia and outdistance her in sophisticated earth satellite systems that could bring more than just propaganda value. What was needed was a way to adapt satellite technology to peaceful uses for humanity the world over. SCORE, transmitting President Eisenhower's Christmas message to the world in 1958, was the beginning.

SCORE – THE TALKING MISSILE

ONE WEEK BEFORE Christmas, 1958, a well-kept secret rode the thundering tailfire of a mighty Atlas intercontinental missile into the evening sky above Cape Canaveral, Florida. Unknown even to tense launch controllers, a unique electronic package, hidden inside a guidance pod on the side of the Atlas, was about to make history.

Slowly, majestically the giant 244,000-pound ICBM lifted from its launch pad at exactly 6:02 P.M. It carried extra fuel, but was lightened somewhat by removal of basic instrumentation normal to a down-range test firing. Straight up it climbed, then gracefully curved over into a trajectory apparently intended for a ballistic flight, aimed at a target area in the South Atlantic Ocean.

A launch technician nervously watched the "bird" start to depart from its normal flight path, under the thrust of its two Rocketdyne booster chambers of 165,000 pounds each.

19

SCORE, world's first "talking satellite," blasts off from Cape Canaveral, Florida, December 18, 1958, to open the Age of Communications Satellites. SCORE carried President Eisenhower's Christmas message to the whole world.

"It's going wild!" he shouted. Already, one missile had veered off course and lunged into the jungles of South America; orders were to destruct the bird if this happened again.

As the Atlas kept climbing higher and higher, it seemed headed for disaster. In alarm, the launch controller jabbed at the red button marked DESTRUCT.

Nothing happened!

As the controller jabbed at the button again and again, he suddenly realized something was wrong—it was disconnected! His fears were calmed, however, by the smiling face of an Air Force officer standing behind him—Major General Bernard A. Schriever, commander of the USAF's Ballistic Missile Division.

"Relax," General Schriever told him. "Everything is green!"

This was the dramatic launch of the world's first successful communications satellite, called SCORE (Signal Communications by Orbiting Relay Equipment). Inside the Atlas's guidance pod were two duplicate packages containing a recorder, radio transmitter and receiver, control unit, batteries and beacon transmitter, developed by the Army Signal Corps and Radio Corporation of America's Astro-Electronics Products Division.

After a lengthened rocket burn of 271 seconds, the Atlas was bodily injected into an orbit with a 115-mile perigee and a 914-mile apogee, looping around the world every 101.5 minutes. But not until the following day did the world realize what had been achieved, when President Dwight D. Eisenhower announced that "the entire vehicle is in orbit ...this success opens new opportunities to the United States and all mankind for activities in outer space."

A still bigger surprise was to come, but this one made headlines. Barely one year earlier, the U.S.S.R. had opened the Space Age by launching its satellite, Sputnik I, into a 96.2-minute orbit. Its chilling electronic "beep...beep...beep" voice was the first communication ever received from outer space. The United States had launched Explorer I on January 31, 1958, and its own small, three-pound Vanguard I scientific satellite on March 17, 1958. Now it had hurtled an entire Atlas, weighing 8,750 pounds, into orbit!

Then, the next day, as the Atlas tumbled end over end more than 100 miles above the Florida coastline on its twelfth orbit, a second shock came. Reporters clustered around a radio at Cape Canaveral, while White House correspondents were invited to a special press conference to hear a broadcast from the SCORE satellite.

Over sizzling static and whistling noises came the voice of President Eisenhower: *"This is the President of the United States speaking ... through the marvels of scientific advance my voice is coming to you from a satellite circling in outer space ..."*

Eisenhower, in the White House, beamed as he sat hunched over a television set beside his press secretary, James C. Hagerty, listening to his prerecorded voice. The voice continued: *"My message is a simple one ... through this unique means I convey to you and to all mankind America's wish for peace on earth and good will toward men everywhere."*

There were still more surprises to come; the SCORE satellite not only broadcast the President's Christmas message to the whole world for demonstration of its unique delayed-repeater capability, it also spanned the continent as a real-time system and carried some 140,000 words of delayed-repeater ("mail bag") traffic before reentry.

A cross-country network of ground stations set up by the U. S. Army talked to each other via courier (recorded) communications from earth to satellite to another earth station. Multiplexed teletype code transmissions, stored on tape in the satellite, were sent to earth on command. Ground stations at Prado Dam Basin, Corona, California, and at Fort Stewart, Georgia, sent voice and teletype messages to each other, using the novel delayed-repeater technique.

Significance of the experiment was to confirm that communications courier satellites could actually provide reliable round-the-world transmission of voice, teletype and even television via ultrahigh frequency (UHF) and microwave, which offered sufficient bandwidth to handle wide-band TV. It was an answer to the highly congested high frequency (HF) band by which worldwide communications then operated.

The reason for this was simple—HF radio waves depended on atmospheric reflectivity (ionospheric scatter) to achieve long range, while non-reflective UHF and microwaves, traveling in a direct line only, were limited in range due to the earth's curvature. By placing TV transmitters on mountaintops, their range of coverage could be extended to about 100 miles, and by broadcasting from an orbiting satellite whole continents and even hemispheres fall within range of line-of-sight transmissions.

Thus, with its delayed-repeater capability, SCORE was able to pick up a message from one ground station, fly across the continent, and relay it back down to another station thousands of miles away.

With this early success of the United States' first experimental communications satellite, in 1958 came the dawn of a new era of instantaneous global communications. There was much to be done to perfect the system, and perhaps SCORE raised more questions than it answered.

What was the best orbit to use? There were three alternatives: 1) A medium-altitude random system, with from 18 to 24 satellites orbiting at from 6,000 to 8,000 miles, to permit communications between major points on earth on practically a full-time basis. 2) A medium-altitude phased system, with controllable satellites ringing earth so that as one disappears over the horizon another reappears. 3) A synchronous system, with one or more satellites in synchronous orbit 22,300 miles above the equator, apparently hanging motionless, neither rising nor setting.

Another question was, should a communications satellite be a simple passive reflector, like a mirror in the sky, or should it be an active repeater, receiving signals from the ground, amplifying them and rebroadcasting them to other ground stations.

The answers to these questions could only come by further experimentation, to find the best arrangement for both civilian and military requirements. Low-cost, high-quality wideband transmission able to cover the globe with voice, teletype, facsimile and TV communications, was the goal of civilian satellites. The military, on the other hand, wanted satellites offering security from celestial eavesdropping. The courier satellites seemed better suited to needs of the Department of Defense.

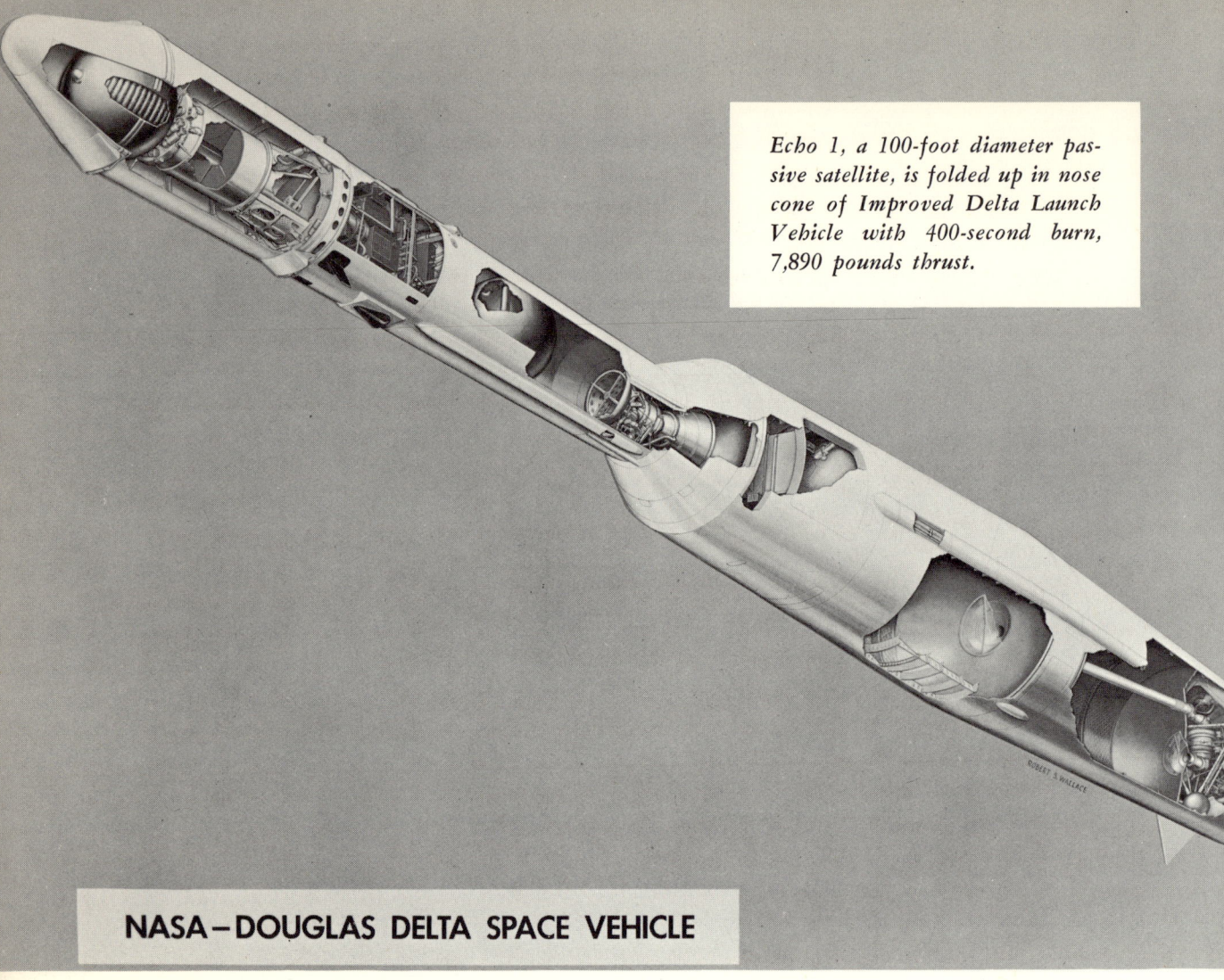

Echo 1, a 100-foot diameter passive satellite, is folded up in nose cone of Improved Delta Launch Vehicle with 400-second burn, 7,890 pounds thrust.

NASA—DOUGLAS DELTA SPACE VEHICLE

LOW-ALTITUDE SATELLITES

IN THE 1950's, two new developments combined to make come true science writer Arthur C. Clarke's prophecy that worldwide radio coverage was not far off. These were a broad-band microwave transmission capability and pioneering communications satellite design able to achieve what Project SCORE showed was possible.

Broad-band microwave transmission also opened a whole new world for television and high-speed information transfer by digital means between distant continents. Recently nine computers in the United States were linked via space to one computer in France; they exchanged eight hours of marketing and financial information in just thirty minutes.

24

ECHO

The success of SCORE in 1958 prompted scientists to explore in earnest different ways that spacecraft could be used for communications purposes. On August 12, 1960, the National Aeronautics and Space Administration launched its first communications satellite, called Echo I. It was little more than a 100-foot-diameter balloon of aluminum-coated mylar polyester plastic, half as thick as the cellophane wrapper on a cigarette package. The NASA satellite weighed 166 pounds.

Folded tightly inside a 26-inch cannister atop a Delta launch vehicle, Echo I was hurled into a near-circular orbit roughly 1,000 miles up, where the balloon was ejected and inflated by a special chemical which changed from a solid to a gas. The author of this book was present at Cape Canaveral to watch the spectacular nighttime launch of this passive communications satellite. It rose smoothly on the dancing tailfire of its 172,000-pound thrust first stage rocket, arced eastward through the night sky, and finally disappeared in the direction of Africa.

Tall as a ten-story house, Echo 1 satellite weighed 116 pounds in orbit, successfully relayed voice and television signals, first satellite to do so.

OSCAR, the ham operator's satellite, is adjusted by members of the TRW Amateur Radio Club prior to launch.

Later on, millions of people would gaze in awe as Echo I, mirroring the sun's rays in early morning or evening, glowed like a tiny moving star. During its seven-and-one-half year lifetime, Echo I grew old and wrinkled under the impact of space dust, but in her youth she served mankind well. For the first time, television programs, photographs and music were broadcast to Echo I and reflected back to distant ground stations, proving that passive communications satellites were feasible.

The second passive satellite, Echo II, was launched on January 25, 1964, from Vandenberg Air Force Base in California, down the Pacific Missile Range and virtually over the South and North Poles. Boosted by a Thor-Agena launcher into an 800-mile orbit, Echo II, weighing 547 pounds, was 135 feet in diameter. Its skin, bonded by aluminum alloy foil, was 50 percent thicker than its predecessor's and was kept youthfully smooth with a controlled inflation system which maintained a constant stress.

Telstar 1, launched July 10, 1962, was first satellite to receive and transmit virtually all kinds of microwave communications—telephone, television, data and facsimile. Built by A.T.&T., Telstar was the first privately owned communications satellite. A nuclear explosion "killed" it.

In the first cooperative space program between the western world and the U.S.S.R., Echo II carried a radio beacon transmitting on 136.021 and 136.170 megacycles. The spacecraft was both optically and electronically tracked in a series of international experiments linking England's Jodrell Bank Observatory with Russia's Zimenki Observatory. This project terminated NASA's experimentation with passive satellites. If their technology was not fruitful, at least they did focus the attention of millions of people on the potential of voices in the sky.

OSCAR

First of a unique series of "talking" satellites called OSCAR (for Orbital Satellite Carrying Amateur Radio) was launched December 12, 1961 by the United States Air Force aboard a Thor-Agena B rocket, riding piggyback with military satellite Discoverer 36. For 18 days OSCAR I broadcast the Morse code signal ...... (Hi) as a greeting to amateur radio operators everywhere. OSCAR II followed, bringing responses from 2,000 radio hams in 35 different countries. OSCAR III was launched March 9, 1965, aboard another scientific satellite and carried a two-meter transponder (transceiver) to qualify also as a communications relay satellite. OSCAR IV, like Courier an active repeater satellite, on December 21, 1965 went into a highly elliptical orbit (101 to 20,847 miles) aboard a Titan IIIC USAF rocket which at the same time orbited two military payloads. These were LES-3 (Lincoln Experimental Laboratory 3), a radio signal generator for satellite systems tests, and LES-4, an experimental, all solid-state satellite.

The OSCAR satellites, dubbed the "poor man's Telstar," cost only $200 to build, enabled amateurs all over the world to converse with each other on VHF line-of-sight frequencies. OSCAR IV was built by members of the TRW-Radio Club of Redondo Beach, California. Headquarters of Project OSCAR is located on the campus of Foothill College, Los Altos Hills, California.

COURIER

The first active repeater satellite capable of signal amplification for retransmission was Courier 1B, lifted into a low orbit of 586 to 767 miles atop a Thor-Able Star, under direction of the U.S. Army Signal Corps, on October 4, 1960. Consistent with its military nature, its repeater system had to be activated by a complex secret code to prevent use by unauthorized governments.

An array of some 20,000 solar cells powered Courier's four transmitters, four receivers, five tape recorders, two telemetry transmitters and its command control system. Its delayed repeater system, which received and transmitted 118,000,000 words during its short 18-day lifetime, was discarded in favor of instantaneous repeaters aboard future communications satellites.

TELSTAR

The decade of the 1960's will be remembered as one of the most revolutionary in the history of technology, largely due to the farsightedness and vigor of the United States' youthful leader, the late President John F. Kennedy. In 1961 Mr. Kennedy dedicated the nation to the gigantic task of putting men on the moon and bringing them back to earth, to achieving commercial supersonic flight, and to bringing the world closer together by hurdling communications barriers with satellites, all in a single decade.

On July 24, 1961, President Kennedy told the nation, "Science and technology have progressed to such a degree that communications through the use of space satellites has become possible...this competence should be developed for global benefit at the earliest practicable time."

Four days later the President's challenge was accepted. The National Aeronautics and Space Administration (NASA) and the American Telephone and Telegraph Company (A.T.&T.) signed an agreement providing for the launch of experimental communications satellites in 1962 as a first step toward practical commercial satellite links. A.T.&T. would provide the satellites, to be built in the Bell Telephone Laboratories, a ground station in Maine, and would assume responsibility for experimentation after the satellites were in orbit. NASA would provide the rockets, the launch pad at Cape Canaveral, Florida, and related tracking and telemetry services. A.T.&T. would pay all costs—about $3,000,000 per launch.

The Maine ground station at Andover was immediately built. A highly sensitive horn reflector antenna was designed to beam signals to an active satellite and receive other signals relayed back. A ruby crystal maser (*m*icrowave *a*mplification by *s*timulated *e*mission of *r*adiation) amplifier, cooled by liquid helium to –456° F., would minimize noise so the antenna could hear the faintest signals coming from the satellite. In addition, another new electronics marvel called a "traveling wave tube" was installed to boost the signal strength as much at 10,000 times.

Meanwhile, the A.T.&T. satellite, *Telstar,* weighing 175 pounds, shaped

TELSTAR Satellite

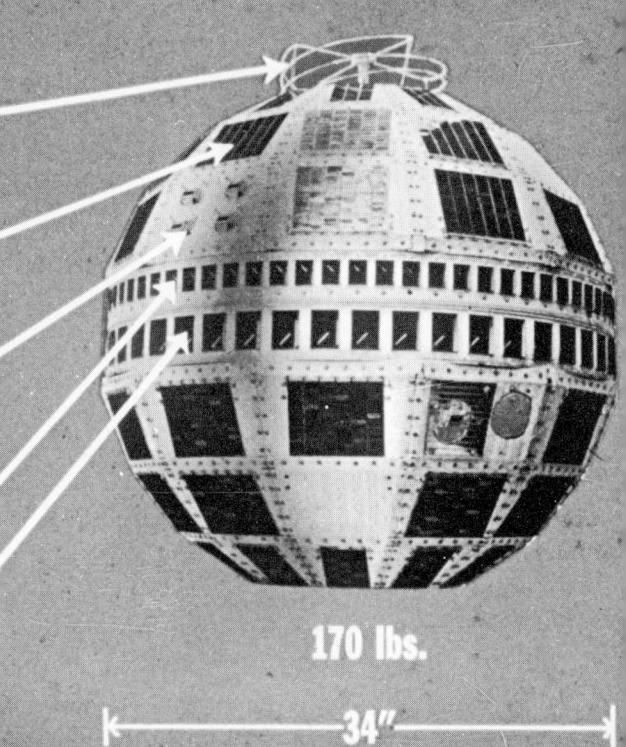

Sends tracking signal and telemetry.
Receives command "on-off" signals.

3600 solar cells convert sun's rays into power.

Measures radiation damage to solar cells.

Receives signal from ground.
Sends signal to ground.

170 lbs.

34"

up in the Bell Telephone Laboratories as a marvel of electronics engineering. A vastly improved active repeater satellite, Telstar was to become the first spacecraft able to receive and transmit virtually all kinds of communications—telephone, television, data and facsimile.

On the early morning of July 10, 1962, Telstar rose into the heavens from Cape Canaveral atop a three-stage Thor Delta rocket and swung into an elliptical orbit ranging between 590 and 3,505 miles in altitude. Later that day it achieved an historic "first" by relaying across the sea to Europe a live television broadcast of President Kennedy at a White House press conference. This was the first of more than 50 TV programs exchanged between the United States and Europe via Telstar.

In one televised program 1,500 doctors attending a convention in Washington, D.C., saw in live color a patient in London and helped diagnose his disease. In another, viewers in America watched the colorful opening of the second Vatican Council in Rome. Less spectacular but more in keeping with Telstar's intended purpose were subsequent

Relay, NASA's first experimental repeater satellite, was first to link North and South America.

test transmissions of one- and two-way telephone conversations, photo-facsimile and high-speed data. The front pages of New York newspapers were relayed by facsimile at a rate of one page per minute, and in one experiment with the graphic arts, Telstar relayed 5,000 words of news copy from New York to Paris at a rate sixteen and one-half times as fast as copy sent by radio or cable. These signals were translated into perforated tape to automatically operate European typesetting machines.

For several months ground stations at Andover, at Holmdel, New Jersey, at Goonhilly Downs, England, at Pleumeur-Bodou, France, and at others located in Italy, Brazil, Germany, Japan, Sweden, and Spain, tracked Telstar's journeys across the heavens—until, in November, 1962, things began to go wrong.

Scientists on earth interrogated Telstar with microwave signals to find out what had happened. The answer came as a shock. Telstar was slowly dying from the effects of a nuclear explosion! On July 9, the day before Telstar was launched from Cape Canaveral, halfway around the world a 1.4-megaton nuclear bomb had been exploded by the United States Atomic Energy Commission 250 miles above Johnston Island. It had released radioactivity that greatly increased the radiation level of a high-altitude natural electromagnetic field known as the Van Allen Belt. This produced serious radio blackouts by increasing background static that would persist for years and lead to a ban on nuclear explosions of such magnitude in space.

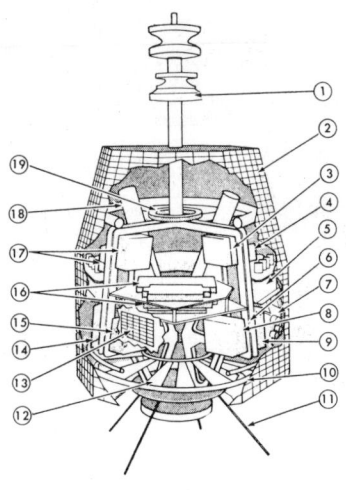
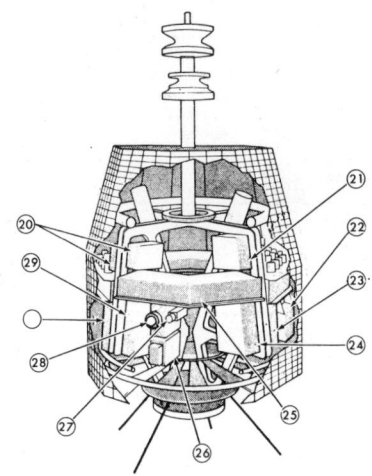

Cutaways showing Relay satellite interior from two angles.

1. BROAD-BAND ANTENNA
2. SOLAR CELLS
3. TELEMETRY TRANSMITTERS
4. BATTERY CHARGE CONTROLLER
5. BATTERY BOX
6. CRUCIFORM STRUCTURE
7. RADIATION DETECTORS B,C,D
8. COMMAND CONTROL UNIT
9. RADIATION SWITCH BOX H
10. TORQUE COIL
    (Adjusts Orientation)
11. TRACKING, TELEMETRY, AND COMMAND ANTENNA
12. THERMAL CONTROLLER
13. RADIATION DAMAGE PANEL
14. RADIATION EFFECTS CIRCUITRY
15. COMMAND RECEIVERS
16. BROAD-BAND RECEIVERS
17. COMMAND DECODERS
18. TRAVELING WAVE TUBE
    (Amplifying Device)
19. PRECESSION DAMPER
    (Reduces Wobble)
20. MICROWAVE BEACONS
21. SIGNAL CONDITIONER
22. RADIATION DETECTORS E,F
23. VOLTAGE REGULATOR
24. TWT POWER SUPPLY
25. TELEMETRY ENCODER
26. SUN ASPECT INDICATOR
    (Indicates Satellite Orientation)
27. HORIZON SCANNER
    (Indicates Satellite Orientation)
28. RADIATION DETECTOR A
29. RADIATION SWITCH BOX G

The first sign of trouble appeared when Telstar's 3,600 solar power cells one by one began to fail. These cells normally recharged the satellite's storage battery with solar energy, to power Telstar's single 2¼-watt vacuum tube and some 1,000 transistors and 1,400 semiconductor diodes. When the solar panels failed, Telstar's voice was choked off and the amazing satellite "died," ceasing communication on February 21, 1963.

Telstar II, five pounds lighter than Telstar I, was launched May 7, 1963. Its electronics, more resistant to radiation, functioned well except for an unexplained period of silence from July 17 to August 12, 1963. Its orbit was more elliptical than that of Telstar I. One day after launch, Telstar II transmitted the first transatlantic color television picture ever sent from America to Europe. It transmitted until May, 1965.

Part of Telstar's legacy is the A.T.&T. ground station at Andover, Maine, with its giant horn so powerful it can send up a signal of 10,000 watts and receive back one as faint as a billionth of a watt. By placing the sophisticated transmitting and receiving equipment on the ground, the satellite itself could be made lighter. Future satellites would in themselves be more powerful, simplifying the design of worldwide ground stations.

RELAY

Relay I, NASA's first experimental repeater satellite, was launched by a Delta rocket from Cape Canaveral on December 13, 1962, into a highly elliptical orbit, ranging from 822 to 4,612 miles. Its orbital inclination of 47.5 degrees meant that it could pass over a ground area extending from 47.5 degrees north latitude to 47.5 degrees south latitude, thus covering most of North and South America. It did, in fact, pioneer satellite communications between the two hemispheres.

With an output of 10 watts, Relay I's voice was stronger than Telstar's, and to prevent further radiation damage as it swung through the highly charged Van Allen Belt, its 8,215 solar cells were coated with quartz. The cells absorbed sunlight and converted it to electricity for charging three nickel cadmium batteries, sufficient power to operate communications experiments 100 minutes per day. In addition, Relay I carried 30 extra solar cells unprotected by quartz, and electronic circuitry, exposed deliberately to report on damage by radiation.

Amazingly enough, when Relay I developed a power drain in one of its two transponders, engineers on earth for the first time were able to make a repair on a satellite in orbit by remote control, turning off the faulty transponder and switching to the alternate. Relay I carried redundant (double) receiving, amplifying and transmitting systems, plus two command systems to increase its chances of survival in the hostile environment of outer space.

In addition to duplicating Telstar's performance of relaying all forms of communications between ground stations over the Atlantic, on November 22, 1963, Relay I transmitted the first live television broadcast across the Pacific. It was a tragic occasion, however, for the prearranged program was to have been a greeting from President Kennedy to the people of Japan. Instead, the Japanese were told of the assassination of President Kennedy only a few hours earlier.

Where news of the assassination of President Lincoln in 1866 took twelve days to reach London, the death of President Kennedy became known to the whole world immediately, via communications satellites.

Relay II, an improved version of Relay I, was launched January 21, 1964, into a low orbit, continuing the experiments of its predecessor. It also provided worldwide coverage of the 1964 Winter Olympics in Europe, the first Japan-France satellite link, first Japanese television transmission by satellite and the 1964 U.S. Presidential election.

In that same year, incidentally, on June 19 President Lyndon B. Johnson of the United States and Prime Minister Hayato Ikeda of Japan conversed by telephone to inaugurate the first submarine cable link between those two countries. Costing $800,000,000, the 5,300-mile link between Tokyo and Honolulu was limited to 128 voice channels. The $37,000,000 link between Hawaii and California had been in service since 1957.

Even as the world hailed this Pacific cable as a vital new link in world communications, scientists knew it could never handle the burden of future traffic. Overseas telephone calls to and from the United States are rising 15 percent annually, and by 1980 some 10,000 circuits will be needed for telephones and a few other services, not including telecasts and high-speed data transfers. Although shortwave radio and undersea cables will continue to play an important role in future communications, they alone cannot keep pace with burgeoning global demands. The answer lies in microwave communications satellites.

Powerful Douglas combination liquid-solid fuel rocket's 333,000-pound thrust, twice that of earlier model, jettisons strapon boosters, streaks into space to launch Syncom III August 19, 1964.

SYNCOMS—THE FIRST SYNCHRONOUS SATELLITES

THE DREAM OF establishing a sychronous satellite communications system, first proposed in 1945, seemed still far in the future in 1959, when a then unknown scientist at Hughes Aircraft Company, Dr. Harold A. Rosen, began tinkering with the idea. There were many problems to overcome —designing a satellite small enough for existing boosters to launch it into a 22,300-mile orbit was just one. There had to be some way to concentrate the synchronous satellite's radiation power so that it would focus on the earth like a celestial flashlight beam, instead of dissipating itself by radiating in all directions.

Dr. Rosen pondered the problem and at last came up with a solution so simple people laughed at him. The secret was in spin-stabilizing a hatbox-shaped satellite and focussing the radio beam by means of a special antenna which directed the transmitter's full energy in a narrow "pancake" beam to earth.

Like other inventors before him—the Wright Brothers, who designed the first flyable heavier-than-air machine, and Simon Lake, who conceived the even-keel submarine—Dr. Rosen found no takers at home.

Discouraged, but not one to give up, Dr. Rosen took his wife and son on a vacation trip to Europe in 1961 and, with a fellow engineer, Thomas Hudspeth, who, along with Don Williams, helped design his curious hatbox satellite, visited the Paris Air Show. There, as a publicity stunt, the two Hughes engineers posed with their device atop the Eiffel Tower. One skeptic snorted, "This is as high as your satellite will ever get!"

Original satellite model was laughed at when Hughes engineers Thomas Hudspeth (l.) and Dr. Harold A. Rosen unveiled it atop Eiffel Tower during 1961 Paris Air Show. "That's as high as it will ever get," skeptics said.

Like a jewel sparkling in the sky, Syncom III was moved into synchronous orbit over the Pacific, relayed the 1964 Olympics from Tokyo to the United States.

However, when NASA decided to back the Hughes Company in a project to build a synchronous satellite, Dr. Rosen was soon in demand. His simple spin technique and disc antenna beam formed the heart of *Syncom I,* a 79-pound satellite 28 inches across. Launched atop a 330,000-pound thrust Delta rocket on Valentine's Day in 1963, the satellite sailed into synchronous orbit 22,300 miles up, but a nitrogen bottle on board apparently exploded. The satellite was silent.

Still convinced the design was right, NASA launched Syncom II on July 26 in the same year. It was a smashing success. President Kennedy inaugurated the satellite with an unprecedented phone call to the prime minister of Nigeria—the satellite hung directly over Africa. Syncom II became the world's first controllable satellite when engineers on earth commanded it to move over South America, under control of a series of gas-jet pulses.

In the spring of 1964 Syncom II was moved still further west, to drift over the International Date Line in mid-Pacific, for experimental transpacific broadcasts. Actually, Syncom II did not achieve a perfect synchronous orbit. The Delta rocket which launched it did not have sufficient thrust to place the satellite exactly on an equatorial orbital plane, though the altitude was correct. Instead, its orbit inclined at 33.1 degrees, so that it appeared to drift overhead through a narrow figure-eight path north and south of the equator.

In order to keep Syncom II from further drifting (there was a limit to the fuel on board to position it), it finally was moved over the Indian Ocean into a unique "gravity trough," where an effect caused by irregularities in the shape of the earth holds the satellite locked in a virtual trap of "triaxiality" gravity forces.

Syncom III went up from Cape Canaveral (renamed Cape Kennedy) August 19, 1964, launched into a perfect synchronous equatorial orbit by a more powerful thrust-augmented Delta (TAD) rocket. One of its first assignments was to relay television coverage of the 1964 Olympic Games from Japan to the United States, and subsequently to Canada and Europe. A Japanese transmitter at Kashima, 50 miles from Tokyo, and a modified Navy dish antenna at Point Mugu, California, were used for this relay.

Maria Wrzesinski peeks into a color cloud camera of Applications Technology Satellite (ATS-1) at Hughes plant where her father is an engineer. ATS pioneered in the development of multiple-access communications satellites and virtual orbiting telephone switchboards.

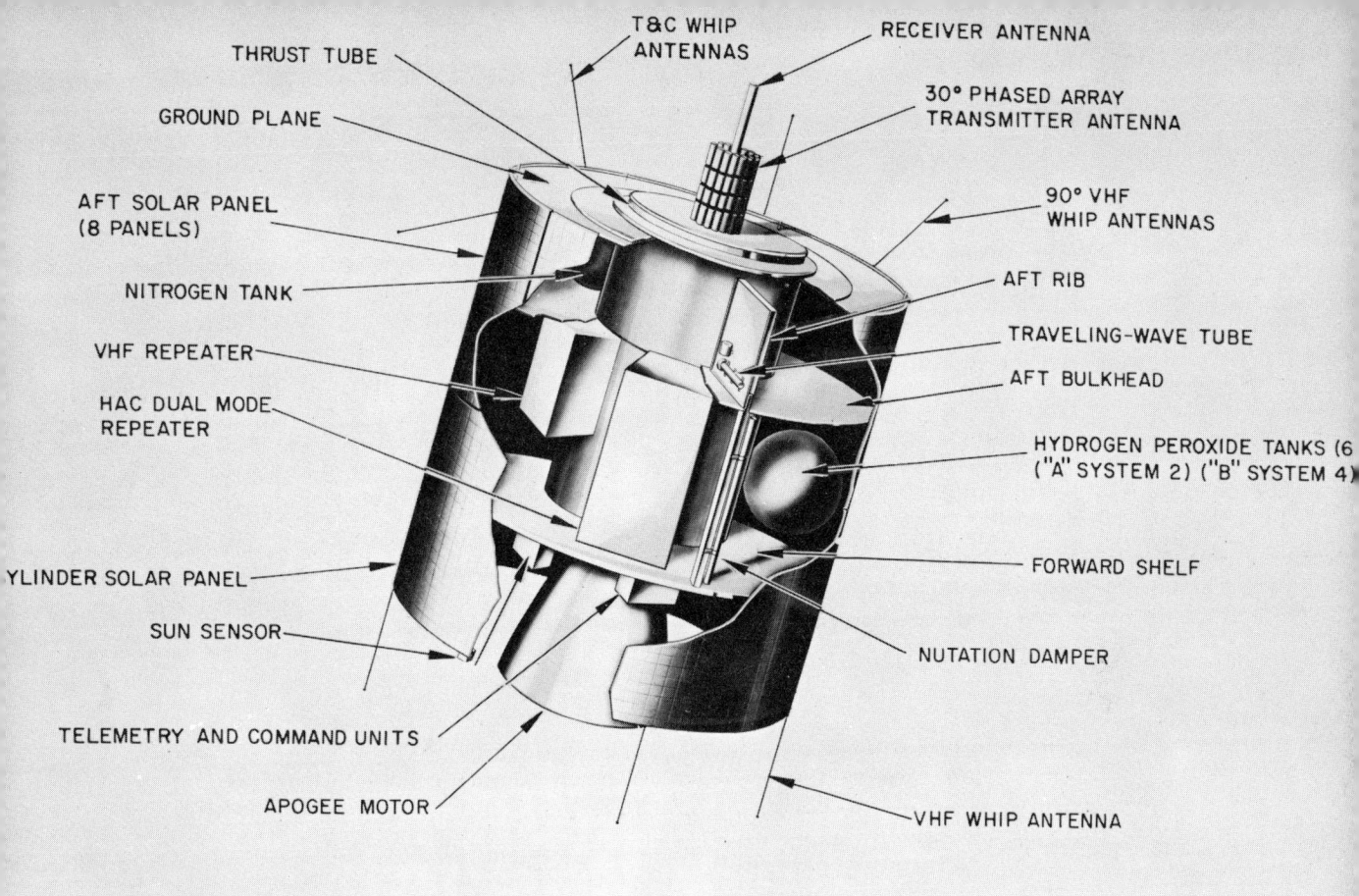

SYNCHRONOUS ALTITUDE SPIN-STABILIZED SPACECRAFT

By remaining apparently motionless in orbit, 86-pound Syncom III opened the way for construction of fixed ground antennas, less expensive to build and operate. Lightweight traveling wave tube amplifiers are used aboard Syncom III.

In order to refine the essential stability characteristics of synchronous satellites, on December 6, 1966, NASA launched a huge new 775-pound Hughes built spacecraft called ATS-1 (Applications Satellite-1) atop an Atlas-Agena D combination rocket. ATS-1 did successfully conduct two-way voice broadcasts between ground stations and distant high-flying jet aircraft, but is best remembered for an amazing televised picture of the entire Pacific hemisphere returned to earth on December 11, 1966.

39

Ships at sea, high-flying aircraft and people on the ground can now be linked via ATS satellites, using small, 75-pound portable unit developed by NASA. Two ten-foot antennas and suitcase-sized walky talky enable man on ground to talk with navigator in aircraft (above) via VHF (Very High Frequency) channel.

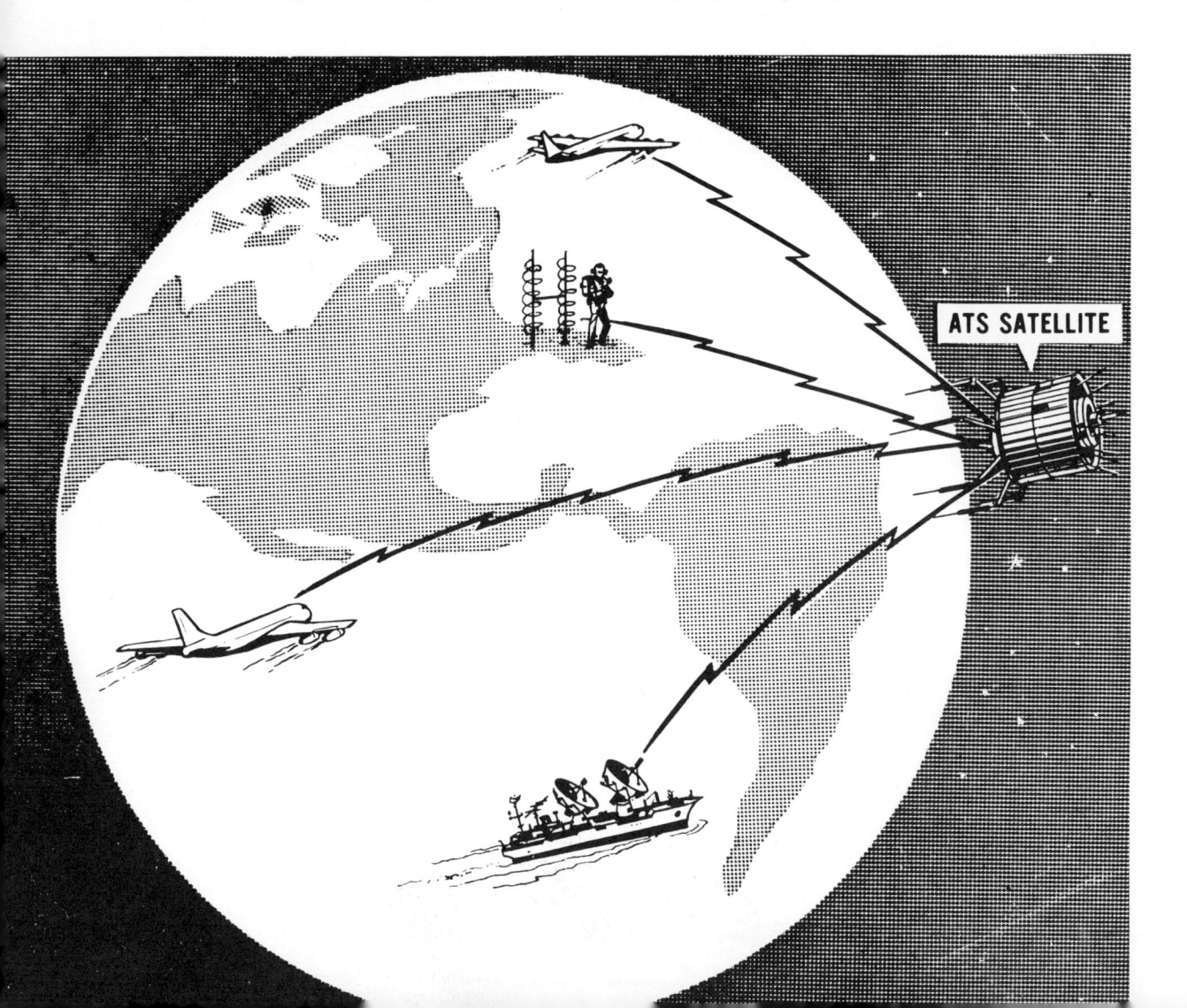

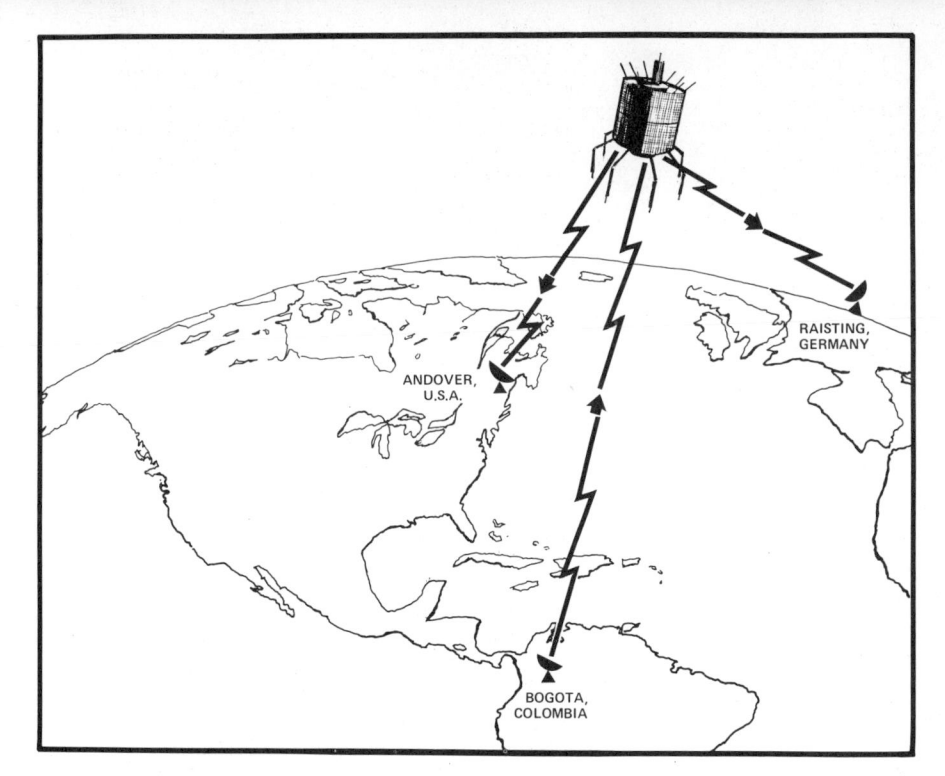

Pope Paul VI's 1968 visit to Bogota, Colombia, was telecast to the world by ATS-3 satellite orbiting 22,300 miles above Brazil's rain forests and ground stations at Andover, Maine, and Raisting, Germany.

Sister Cecelia Louise, a Ph.D. in science, tries out portable TV ground station (electronic van and 16-foot dish antenna) shipped to Bogota for Pope Paul VI's visit. The broadcast was in live color.

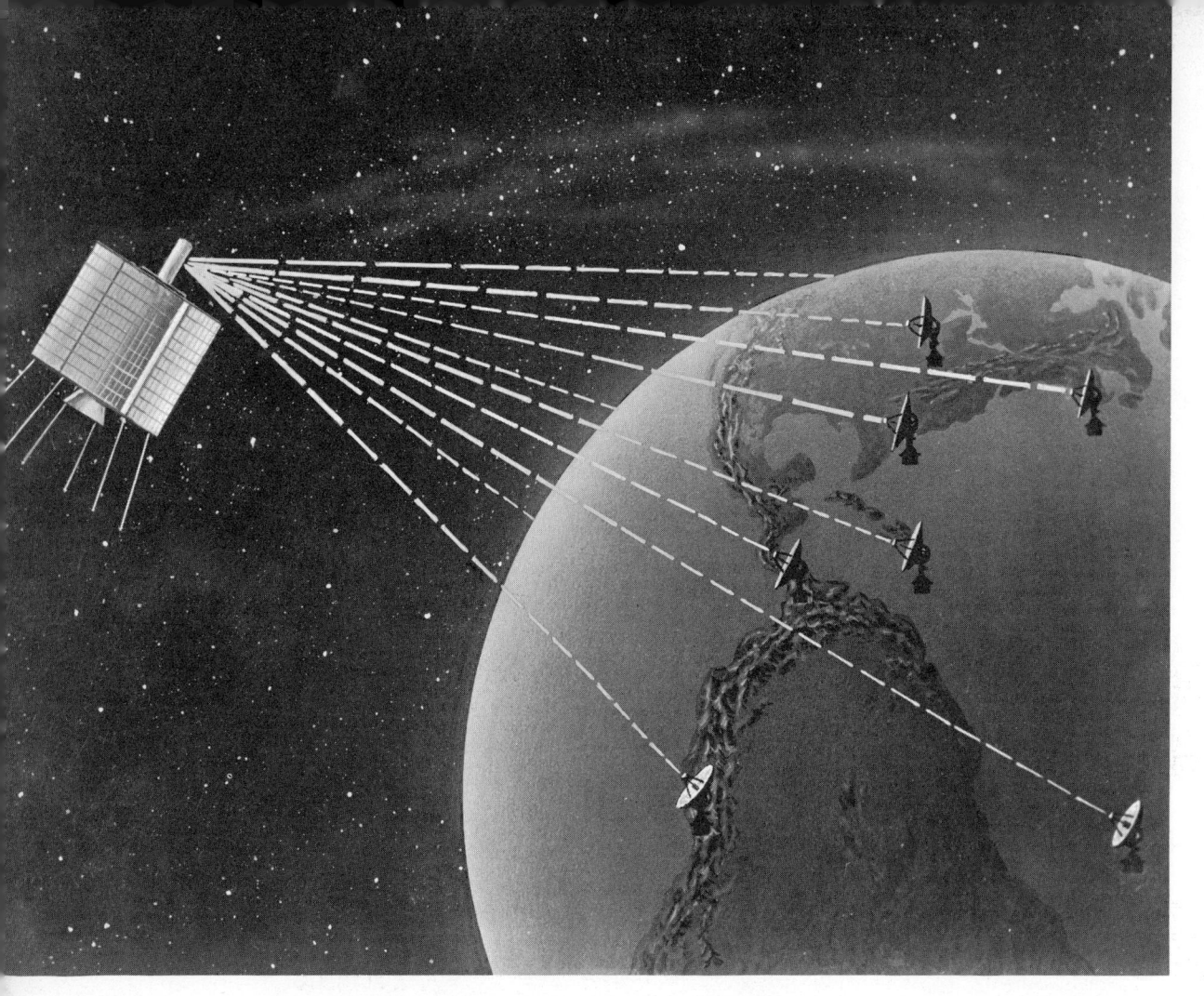

How multiple-access communications satellite works. Circuits are automatically assigned to link any two pairs of earth stations in response to actual traffic demand, making it a virtual orbiting switchboard.

ATS-2, launched April 5, 1967, was supposed to go into a 6,000-mile circular orbit to study a unique gravity gradient stability system at medium altitude, but failed to do so when the Agena rocket booster failed to restart. It ended instead in a looping elliptical orbit of 115-6,947 miles.

ATS-3 on November 5, 1967, achieved a synchronous equatorial orbit, being positioned at 60 degrees west longitude over the Amazon rain forests. With a capacity of 1,200 one-way, or 600 two-way, voice circuits, ATS-3 was expected to help make possible multiple-access communications, when associated switching circuits on the ground are tied in. One of the most significant new technologies under development, the multiple-access repeater will allow many ground terminals to use the satellite at the same time, making it a virtual "telephone exchange" in orbit. Such a multiple access capability could be operational by 1970, say designers of the ATS satellites.

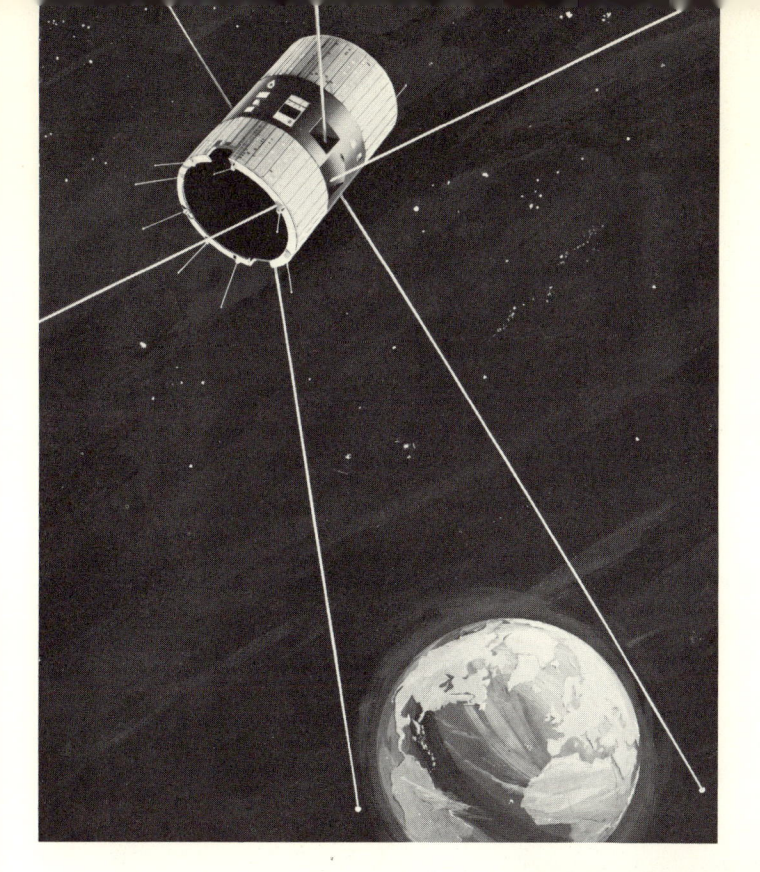

ATS "gravity gradient" satellite, planned for 1969 launch, uses 250-foot telescoping metal booms like a tight-rope walker's pole to hang motionless in synchronous orbit. Booms offset rotation torque.

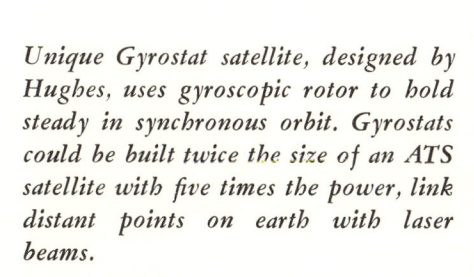

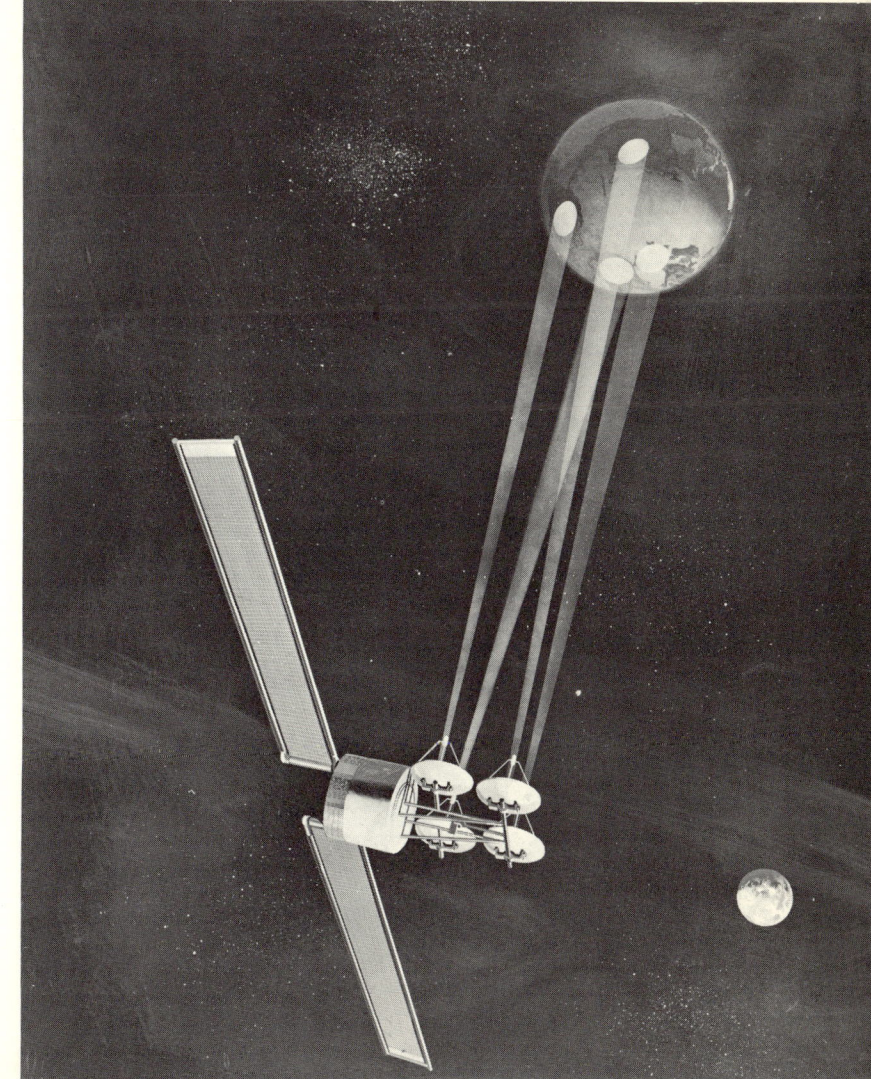

Unique Gyrostat satellite, designed by Hughes, uses gyroscopic rotor to hold steady in synchronous orbit. Gyrostats could be built twice the size of an ATS satellite with five times the power, link distant points on earth with laser beams.

COMMERCIAL SATELLITES ARRIVE

UNQUALIFIED SUCCESS OF A.T.&T.'s Telstar communications satellite made clear that the future of voices in the sky was already at hand in the summer of 1962. There were "doubting Thomases" in Congress, however, who feared that a bill authorizing creation of a private corporation to own and operate future satellites would give A.T.&T. a space monopoly. Despite a filibuster by obstructionists, the bill, containing safeguards against monopoly, became law on August 31 under President Kennedy's signature.

On August 31, 1962, the late President John F. Kennedy signed into law the Communications Satellite Act, creating the Communications Satellite Corporation.

Early Bird, the world's first commercial synchronous satellite, views one third of earth's surface from position above Atlantic. It links U.S. station at Andover, Maine, to European stations at (2) Goonhilly Downs, England; (3) Pleumeur-Bodou, France; (4) Raisting, West Germany; (5) Fucino, Italy.

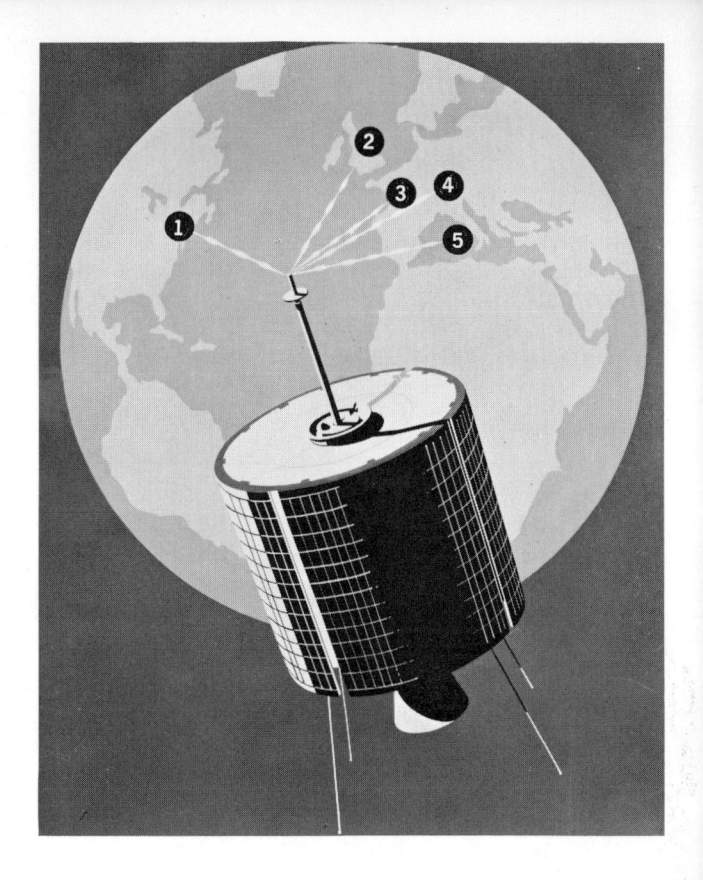

Early Bird satellite was spin-stabilized, precisely oriented during six elliptical orbits before apogee motor was fired, thrusting it into circular earth orbit. Satellite was then tilted to direct strongest signals over the North Atlantic.

EARLY BIRD ORBITAL DYNAMICS

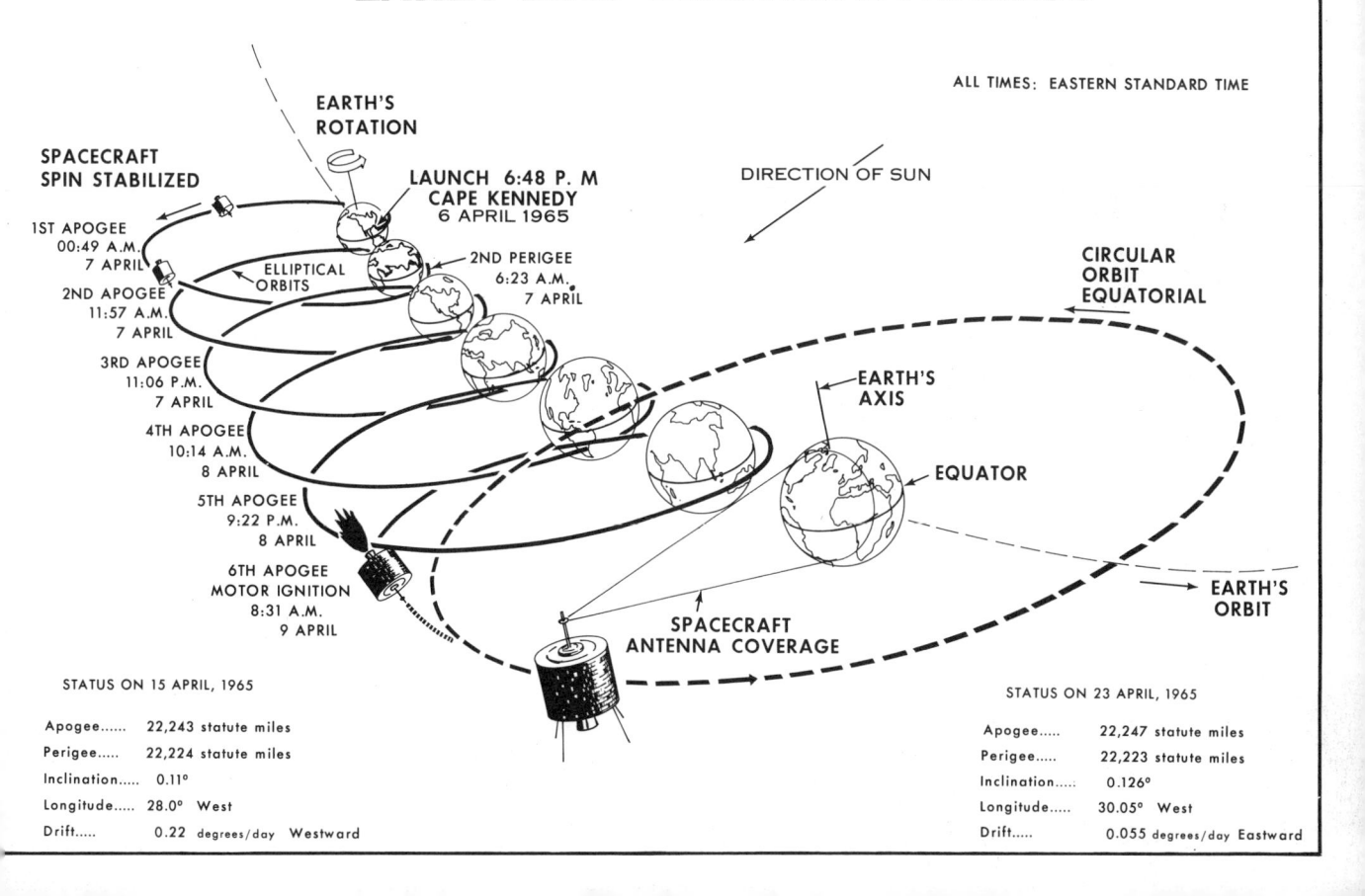

ALL TIMES: EASTERN STANDARD TIME

EARTH'S ROTATION
SPACECRAFT SPIN STABILIZED
LAUNCH 6:48 P.M CAPE KENNEDY 6 APRIL 1965
1ST APOGEE 00:49 A.M. 7 APRIL
ELLIPTICAL ORBITS
2ND PERIGEE 6:23 A.M. 7 APRIL
2ND APOGEE 11:57 A.M. 7 APRIL
3RD APOGEE 11:06 P.M. 7 APRIL
4TH APOGEE 10:14 A.M. 8 APRIL
5TH APOGEE 9:22 P.M. 8 APRIL
6TH APOGEE MOTOR IGNITION 8:31 A.M. 9 APRIL

DIRECTION OF SUN
CIRCULAR ORBIT EQUATORIAL
EARTH'S AXIS
EQUATOR
EARTH'S ORBIT
SPACECRAFT ANTENNA COVERAGE

STATUS ON 15 APRIL, 1965

Apogee...... 22,243 statute miles
Perigee..... 22,224 statute miles
Inclination..... 0.11°
Longitude..... 28.0° West
Drift..... 0.22 degrees/day Westward

STATUS ON 23 APRIL, 1965

Apogee..... 22,247 statute miles
Perigee..... 22,223 statute miles
Inclination..... 0.126°
Longitude..... 30.05° West
Drift..... 0.055 degrees/day Eastward

Andover, Maine ground station, inside radome, has 380-ton cornucopia-like "horn of plenty" to talk with synchronous satellites. Small dish on framework was used to turn on Early Bird.

Fucino, Italy's ground station has new 90-foot dish antenna, is capable of handling all types of telephone, television and data transmissions across the Atlantic.

Intelsat II's odd biconical horn antenna (left) permits multiple-access to messages, TV programs, instead of rotating transmissions among nations. Hughes engineers (right) check out Intelsat II's antennas, which handle 125-megacycle bandwidth signal amplified by four six-watt traveling wave tubes.

This bill, the Communications Satellite Act of 1962, created a new and unique private corporation as an instrument of the United States to establish a commercial communications satellite system as quickly as possible. Services were to be made available to other countries without discrimination. Details were left up to the President, the State Department and to the new corporation, formed a few months later, with Dr. Joseph V. Charyk, former Under Secretary of the United States Air Force, as president.

Known as the Communications Satellite Corporation, or Comsat, the giant young government-regulated business was capitalized in June, 1964, through issuance of 10,000,000 shares of common stock at $20 a share. Half went to established communications carriers, the other half to the public—more than 138,000 individual investors in this first Space Age corporation.

In August of 1964 a joint international venture, the International Telecommunications Satellite (Intelsat) Consortium, was born. Within a month 14 nations joined Intelsat, and by late 1968 the number had blossomed to 63.

A ring of four Intelsat III satellites provides long-sought goal of global communications for all nations. Each can handle 6,000 circuits, or a dozen color TV broadcasts at once.

Portable three-foot ground terminal dish antenna folds into shoulder packs carried by two men, for military, educational or disaster control remote broadcasting.

Participants in Intelsat jointly own the satellites of the global system, while ground stations are owned by individual nations and, in the case of the United States and Japan, by private corporations. Actual operations did not commence until April 6, 1965, when Comsat, as manager for Intelsat, launched *Early Bird*, the world's first commercial communications satellite.

Three days after launch Early Bird was shifted from its elliptical into a synchronous orbit so perfect it completed each trip around earth in 23 hours 57 minutes, only 56 seconds off. Before becoming fully commercial on June 28, Early Bird showed its capabilities by relaying color television broadcasts, transmitting news photos from London to New York and staging an international art auction, with customers in the Parke-Bernet Galleries in New York bidding on art objects at Sotheby's in London.

Providing 240 high-quality, two-way voice channels (equal to one color TV channel), Early Bird, positioned over the mid-Atlantic, was turned on by a command from the Andover, Maine, ground station to become the first link in a growing worldwide network of commercial communications satellites.

A mechanical and electronic marvel, Early Bird possessed six times the effective radiated power of Syncom III, 50 percent larger solar panels and a life expectancy extended from 18 months at launch to from five to ten years as its systems proved to be smoothly functioning. The satellite's traveling wave tube, making possible signal amplification as much as 10,000 times, opened the way to a remarkable list of achievements. By mid-1968, five years after launch, it had:

• Relayed more than 220 hours of television.

• Carried thousands of phone calls, data and record messages over 162 leased voice-grade circuits.

• Transmitted live coverage of Pope Paul's historic visit to the United States in 1965.

• Provided on-location coverage of Gemini spacecraft splashdowns in the Atlantic in 1965-66.

• Enabled millions of viewers in Europe and America to watch history in the making via more than 100 special news telecasts.

• Relayed weather map facsimiles from Washington to Paris eight times faster than by conventional radio or cable.

Early Bird was followed by three more communications spacecraft of the Intelsat II series in 1967. Like Early Bird, they were also built by Hughes on Dr. Rosen's design, but were twice as large and with more than twice the power. Special multiple-access antennas permitted the Intelsat II satellites to operate simultaneously with several earth stations.

Like Early Bird, the Intelsat II satellites retained the 240-channel capacity, but added power permitted a greater geographical coverage.

First of the 1967 launches on January 11 positioned the first Intelsat II, *Pacific I*, near 173 degrees east longitude for service over the Pacific. The second, *Atlantic II*, was launched March 22; it joined Early Bird in mid-Atlantic, near 8 degrees west longitude. The third, *Pacific II*, launched September 27, was positioned near 175 degrees east longitude to expand commercial service in the Pacific area. It could be repositioned over either ocean in an emergency.

Costing Intelsat members more than $2,000,000 each, these remarkable satellites capable of providing 25 watts of power with two traveling wave tubes operating, also provided communications support for America's moon shot—Project Apollo.

SNAP 8DR prototype space reactor may presage long-life nuclear power supply for orbiting satellites. Control elements (shaded) regulate hot core (center).

Gigantic Intelsat IV, nearly 18 feet tall, dwarfs small Syncom, world's first synchronous satellite conceived by Dr. Harold A. Rosen of Hughes Aircraft Co.

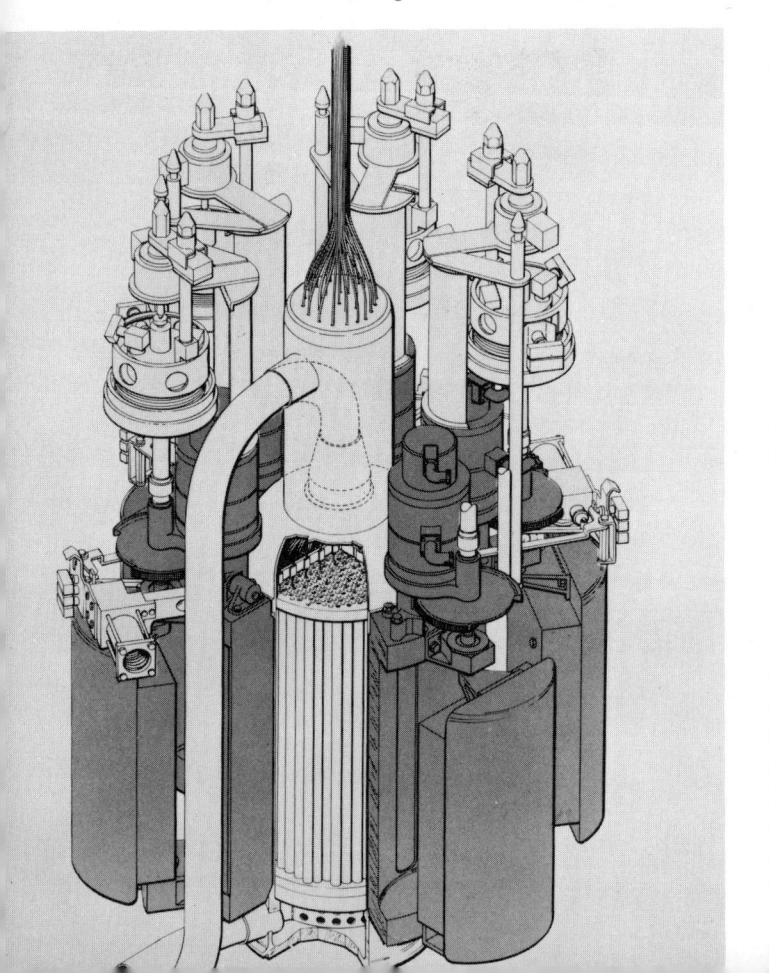

Early in 1966 Comsat, as manager for Intelsat, entered into a $32,375,000 contract with TRW Systems of Redondo Beach, California, to produce six uprated satellites with five times the channel capacity of Intelsat II. These third generation commercial satellites weighed 608 pounds at launch, 303 pounds in orbit. Electrical power from a storage battery and solar arrays of 10,720 solar cells gave Intelsat III more than 158 watts of effective radiated power at synchronous altitude. As the satellite spun clockwise, its antenna mechanically despun counterclockwise at precisely the same speed, thus focusing its communications beam toward earth.

In all, four Intelsat III's were to be launched into synchronous equatorial orbits, the remaining two being standbys. The first was intended to join Early Bird and Atlantic II, at 31 degrees west longitude, over the Atlantic. The second was planned to orbit over the Pacific at 174 degrees east longitude, near Pacific I and Pacific II. The third was to hang above the Atlantic at six degrees west longitude, and the fourth over the Indian Ocean, at 62.5 degrees west longitude. With the four satellites already in operation, the new network of four Intelsat III's would achieve the long-sought goal of global communications for all nations.

The initial Intelsat III launch was a failure, through no fault of its own. Shortly after lift-off from Cape Kennedy, the new-type Delta launch vehicle exploded, setting back the tight launch schedule. The second Intelsat III moved into the dead "bird's" position for duty over the Atlantic, and even as this was being done, a new $72,000,000 contract with Hughes Aircraft Company, builders of Early Bird and the Intelsat II series, was announced, to begin construction of a monster new Intelsat IV, for launch early in the 1970's.

In keeping with Intelsat's global nature, $19,000,000 in subcontracts were let to suppliers in ten nations—Canada, Britain, France, West Germany, Japan, Italy, Switzerland, Belgium, Sweden and Spain. This first true "global" satellite was designed to have 25 times the communications capacity of Intelsat II—6,000 circuits able to handle as many telephone calls simultaneously, or a dozen color TV broadcasts at once.

A unique design feature of Intelsat IV is its ability to focus power into a pair of "spotlight" beams and point them at any selected areas within the visible hemisphere, providing stronger signals and more channel capacity where heaviest communications traffic demands. This focussing of power—more than 3,000 watts per beam channel—will enable small, emerging nations to join the Intelsat network at nominal expense.

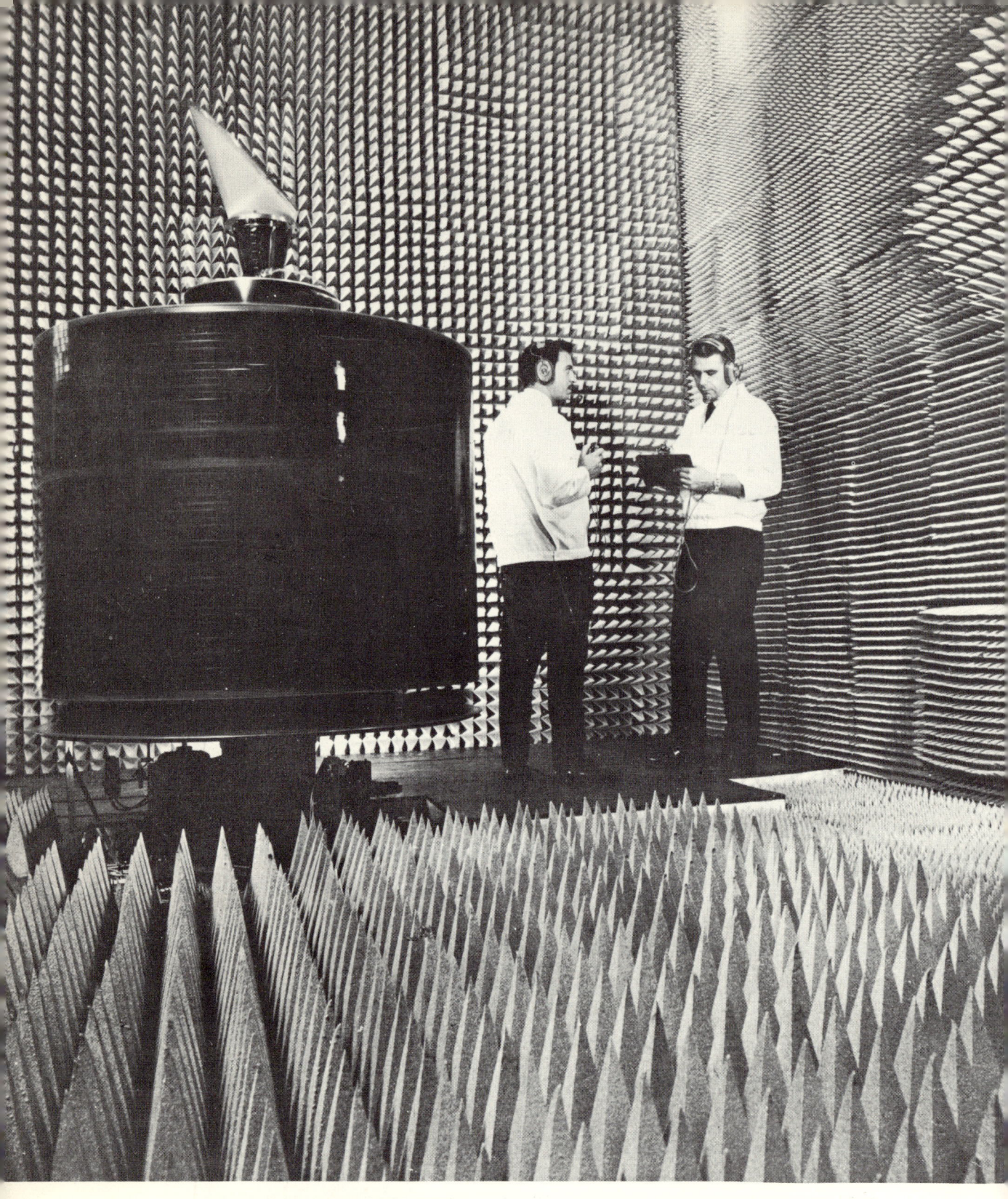

An INTELSAT III series satellite is shown as it underwent final tests in the anechoic (echo-free) chamber at TRW, manufacturers of the INTELSAT III series satellites. Each of these satellites has a design capacity of 1,200 two-way voice circuits and has a life expectancy of five years. Spikes are of rubberized hog's hair.

Such futuristic satellites are now possible because of availability of bigger rocket boosters to put heavier weights into synchronous orbits. Intelsat IV, weighing 2,452 pounds at lift-off, is designed for launch by a Titan-IIIB/Agena combination rocket. Eight feet in diameter and almost 18 feet tall, it features two steerable dish antennas, controllable on command from earth, to provide spot beam broadcast capability. Intelsat IV will be able to move over any part of the world along the equator to serve as an active repeater link where traffic demands.

Even as work started on Intelsat IV, a White House task force, headed by Eugene V. Rostow, Under Secretary of State for Political Affairs, began a review of the United States communications policy, in view of other plans to spend more than $100,000,000 on a fifth transatlantic telephone cable.

Equatorial synchronous satellite corridor by 1969 already was getting crowded as Intelsats 1, 2 and 3 established global network. Frequency allocations are important to prevent interference as Russia's Intersputnik network and proposed domestic satellites complete the electronic "necklace."

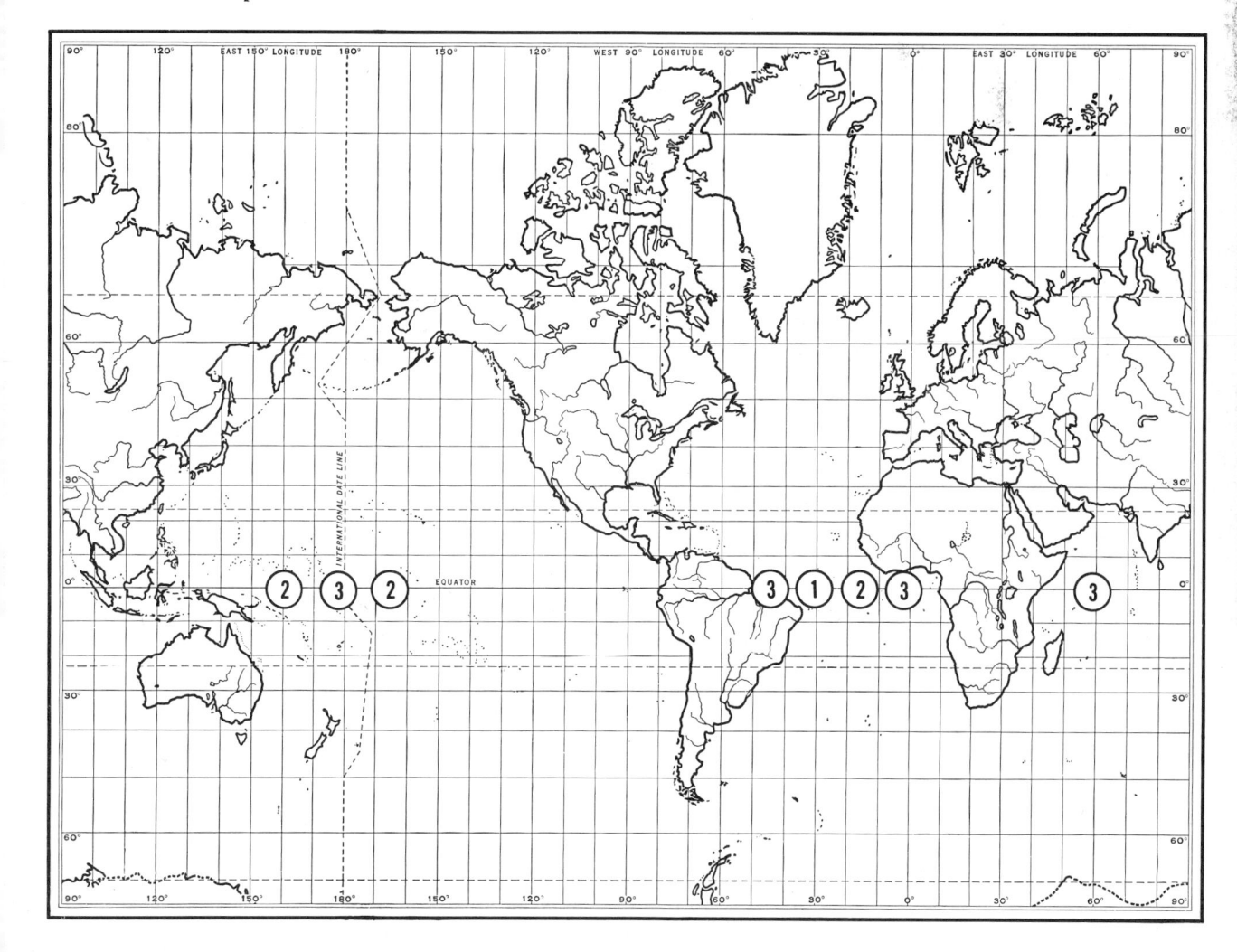

Another area to be resolved was that of putting up domestic communications satellites, rather than global systems, capable of beaming TV programs directly into homes and in other ways replacing overcrowded land lines and microwave relay links.

A dozen companies and organizations, led by the American Broadcasting Company and the Ford Foundation, have sought government approval to launch their own satellites to distribute TV programs, commercial and educational. Comsat itself proposed such a domestic satellite system, using two high-capacity satellites such as Intelsat IV, operating with 30 earth stations, to provide 12 color TV channels, including two educational TV channels, or 21,600 message channels. A full-scale domestic satellite system, Comsat proposed, could consist of four high-capacity satellites operating with more than 150 earth stations to provide 16 commercial TV channels, four educational TV channels, and 28,000 message channels.

By the late 1970's nuclear power sources aboard satellites may make possible breathtaking new communications links, including picturephones in every home. Manned orbiting satellite switchboards, first proposed in 1945 by Arthur C. Clarke, are a distinct possibility.

Other future plans for satellite communications are equally intriguing. A Satellite World University has been proposed, with eminent lecturers bringing new knowledge to all corners of the globe. Politicians, however, worry that these same facilities might be used unwisely for propaganda purposes.

One ingenious design for future satellites is the Hughes gyrostat system, which utilizes the stabilizing effect of a gyroscope rotor to hold the device steady in space. Such giant spinning satellites could carry antennas, laser (*l*ight *a*mplification by *s*timulated *e*mission of *r*adiation) beams, telescopes and solar panels independently aimed in any direction to give greatest flexibility of use.

By the year 2000, the equatorial sky could be ringed with satellites like a necklace of pearls, both for global and domestic communications. Hence, international control of all assigned frequencies would be required.

One proposal has been made to position a satellite in the libration center of the earth-moon gravitational system, where combined gravity forces would hold it steady with relation to both bodies.

Because of this danger of overcrowding the heavens, fewer supersized satellites able to handle up to 100,000 channels may be the ultimate answer to space communications. Whatever its final form, the future is being built today. In August of 1967, the President of the United

States appealed to the Soviet Union and the nations of Eastern Europe to join Intelsat to prevent international communications anarchy. The goal, said President Johnson, was to assure that satellite positions in orbit could be assigned, frequencies allocated and energy from satellites controlled to prevent interference with other communications systems.

Already in the fall of 1968 there were 22 earth stations operating in 14 countries. It is expected that 70 earth stations will be in service in the early 1970's. True global service, in 1969, with completion of the Intelsat III network, bears out President Kennedy's 1961 prophecy that the world would be linked by communications satellites in this decade.

In a world where there are more TV sets than telephones, however, the most dramatic innovation will come when domestic communications satellite service is achieved.

Doctors the world over actually watched Dr. Michael DeBakey, noted Houston, Texas, heart specialist, perform open-heart surgery via Intelsat relay system.

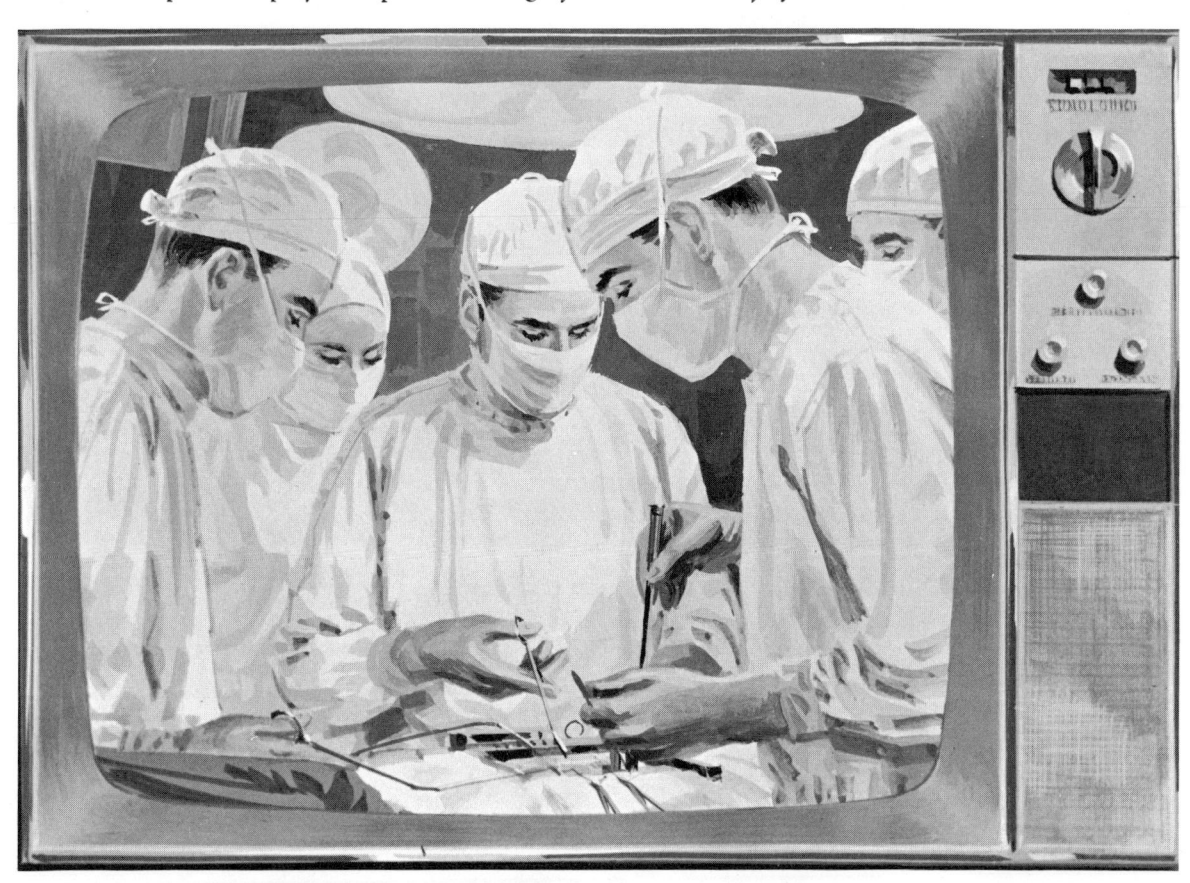

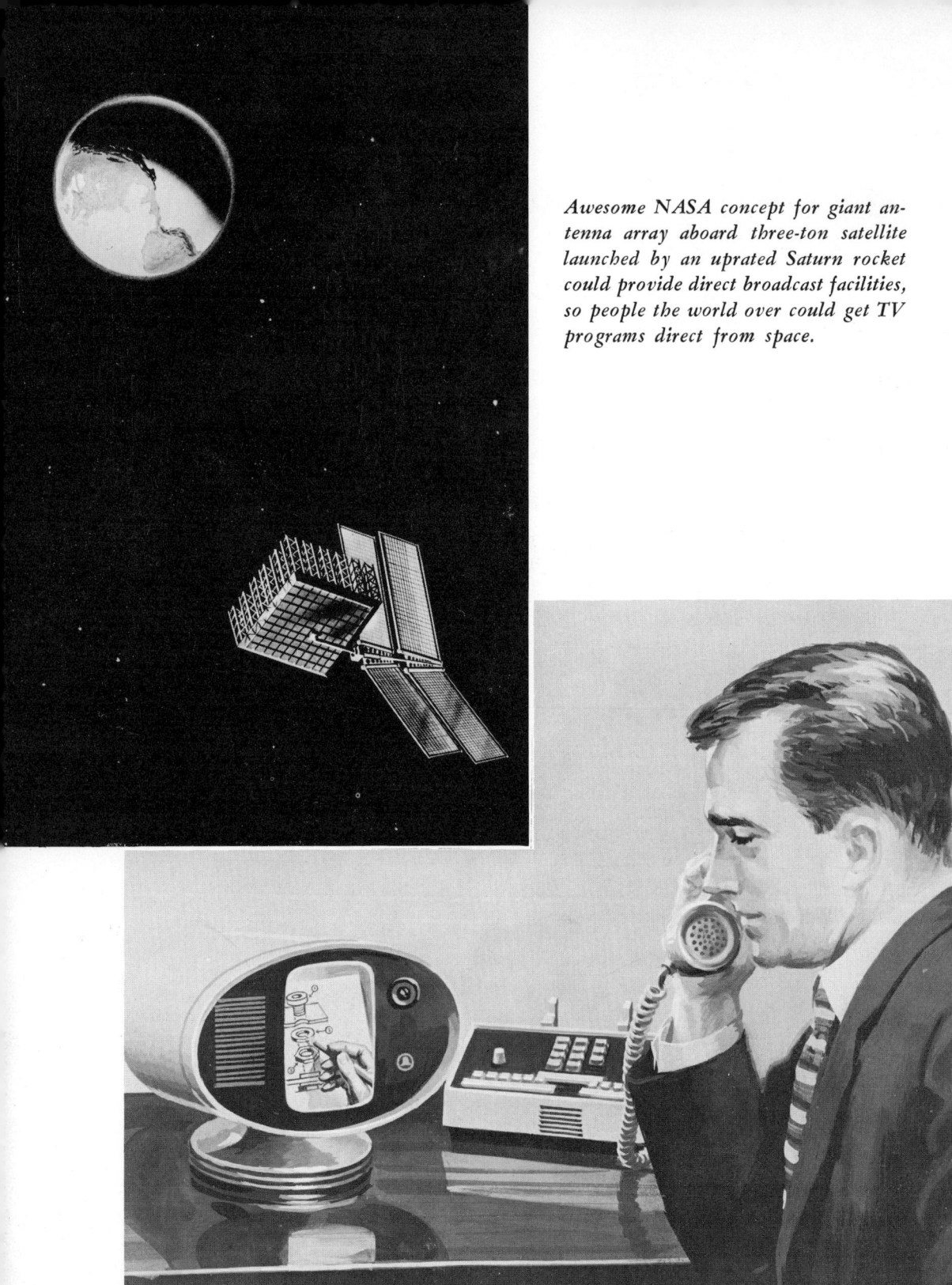

Awesome NASA concept for giant antenna array aboard three-ton satellite launched by an uprated Saturn rocket could provide direct broadcast facilities, so people the world over could get TV programs direct from space.

Picture-phones, developed by Bell Laboratories, are now possible for global communications via Intelsat III and IV satellites.

RUSSIAN LIGHTNING IN THE SKY

EARLY IN THE morning of April 23, 1965, a giant Soviet rocket launcher lifted from its pad at Tyura Tam in central Asia, swung northeast and injected into a highly elliptical orbit with an apogee nearly one earth diameter away, high over the frozen northern latitudes.

The "bird" was Molniya-1A, the first Russian communications satellite, designed to arc high and hang in the sky as an active repeater system 12 hours a day. By the fall of 1968 a total of eight Molniyas were rising above the horizon, one after the other, providing the vast Union of Soviet Socialist Republics with the world's first national communications satellite system.

Completing the network were 24 ground stations—from Moscow in the west to Petropavlousk in the east, from Murmansk in the north to Frunze in the south. Two of the stations, at Moscow and at Vladivostok, are key stations with command and telemetry equipment to control Molniya's onboard transmitter and receiver.

The Molniya itself, a tapering cylinder with six radiating solar panels, has an odd spider-like appearance. It carries two three-foot diameter

Russia's Orbita domestic satellite system links 23 ground stations to Moscow, bringing live TV into Soviet homes from Murmansk in frozen north to Alma-Ata and Irkutsk in Central Asia, eastward 6,000 miles to Kamchatka Peninsula, via Molniya 1 satellites.

Soviet Molniya 1 spacecraft works 12 hours a day as active repeater satellite in 24,000-mile high elliptical orbit. Two three-foot parasol antennas can aim 40-watt transmitter beams. Molniya is controlled from Moscow and Vladivostok, brings the Bolshoi ballet into homes in Siberia.

Spider-like Molniya 1's six solar panels convert sunlight into electrical energy to link the U.S.S.R. with European stations. It could also reach North America.

parasol antennas which can be remotely aimed to direct narrow beams from onboard relay transmitters of 40-watts power. This high power comes from three traveling wave tubes, and is nearly 20 times as strong as the signals from Early Bird, which went into orbit just eleven days before Molyniya-1A.

Molniya-1B, orbited October 14, 1965, provided the first Soviet-France satellite link, one on which voice, television and teletype circuitry can operate. In the winter of 1966, incidentally, the author visited Moscow, and at the Metropole Hotel watched a televised program from France, showing Premier Aleksei Kosygin visiting the Sud Aviation aircraft plant at Toulouse, where the Anglo-French Concorde SST was nearing completion. The picture quality was good.

Molniya-1C, launched April 26, 1966, carried television camera equipment with which to photograph cloud formations, thus serving a dual role as both a communications and meteorological satellite.

In November, 1967, on the fiftieth anniversary of the Bolshevik Revolution, Russia's nationwide Orbita television system went into operation, utilizing the Molniya satellites to beam programs from Moscow to the other 23 ground stations, stretching a quarter way around the globe. Government-controlled programming, largely music and propaganda, now also brings such attractions as the Bolshoi Ballet to remote areas of distant Siberia—live. In 1968 steps were taken to adapt 22 of the Orbita network stations to receive facsimile transmissions and to handle an automatic telephone network with multiple station access.

The Orbita ground stations operate 15-meter aluminum alloy antennas designed to function at temperature extremes from –55 to 115 degrees Fahrenheit, in the rigorous climates of Siberia to Central Asia.

Molniya—the name means "lightning" and refers to "news flashes" in Soviet slang—functions as a sophisticated Space Age satellite system in a primitive and pioneer country where surface microwave relays would be too expensive to build. Its success has led the Soviets to plan a global communications satellite system in competition with Intelsat, to be called *Intersputnik.*

On August 5, 1968, the United Nations Committee on the Peaceful Uses of Outer Space received a draft agreement calling for formation of Intersputnik, signed by delegates from the USSR, Mongolia, Bulgaria, Cuba, Czechoslovakia, Hungary, Poland and Romania. In it the Soviets proposed to establish a "one-nation-one-vote" membership, in contrast to Intelsat, which operates on an investment-use basis. Intersputnik also proposed to coordinate with the International Telecommunication Union and other international organizations utilizing satellites, to insure non-conflicting use of frequency spectrums and other technical matters.

Because many of the potential Intersputnik member nations are in such distant places as Africa and South America, the system would require satellites in synchronous orbit, adding to the growing "string of pearls" of Intelsats now above the equator.

Whatever the future of Intersputnik, its technology goes back to Russia's Molniya-Orbita experience, in which high-power (40-watt) transmitters make possible smaller and simpler ground station designs.

Other nations have proposed designing, building and launching their own systems, notably a Canadian and a French-German project called

Molniya 1 Soviet satellites also have TV cameras to watch for storms. Ability to reach the African continent is revealed in this Cosmos 144 satellite TV picture of the Nile River, Red Sea and Sinai Peninsula made in 1967.

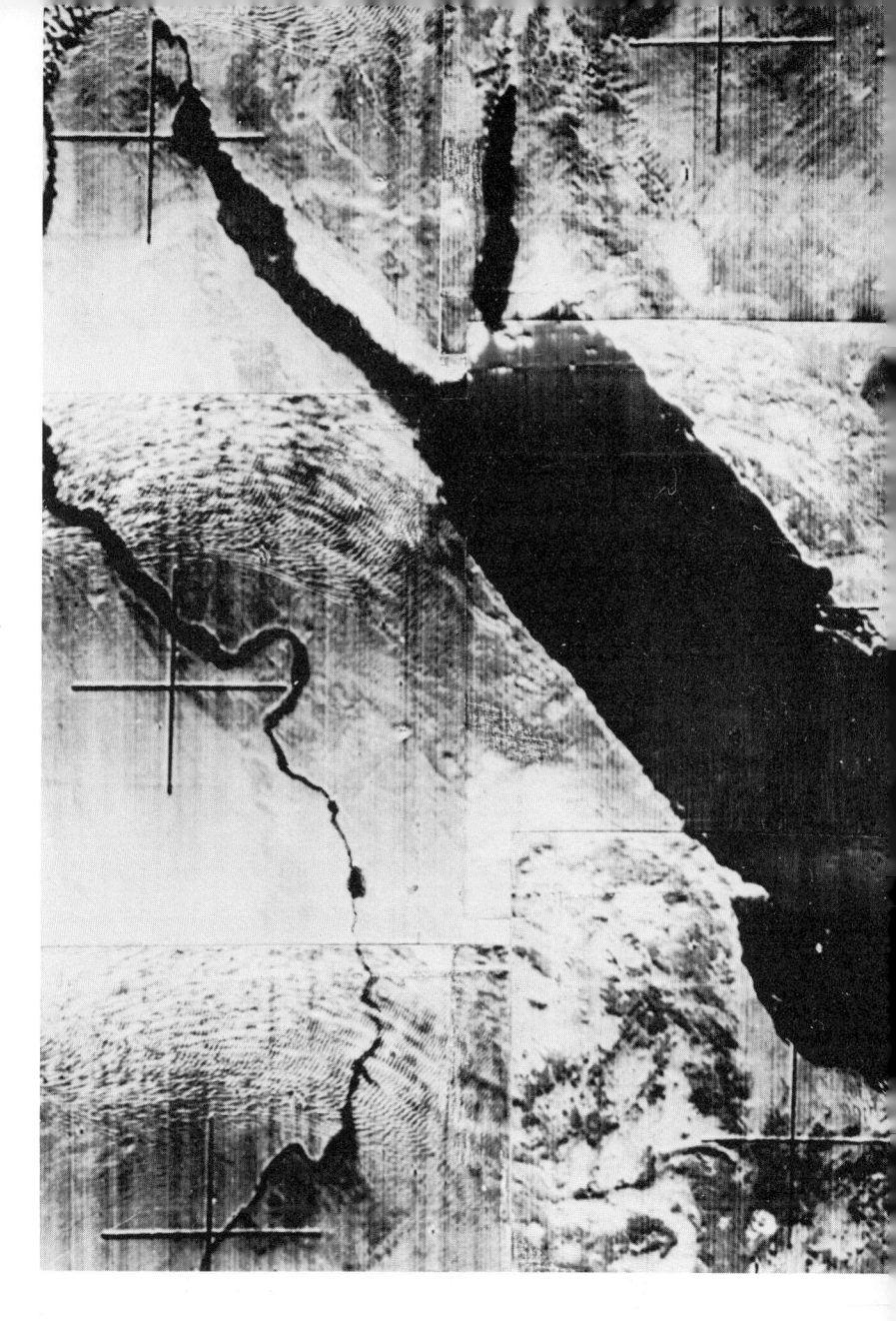

Symphonie. In 1967 Eurospace, the European aerospace industry association, also proposed the formation of a regional system to be called *Eurosat.*

In the final analysis, communications satellites have opened exciting new possibilities for expanding man's understanding of other peoples. In the words of the President of the United States, on August 14, 1967, "The communications satellite knows no geographic boundary, is dependent on no cable, owes allegiance to no single language or political philosophy. Man now has it within his power to speak directly to his fellow man in all nations."

To the Soviets, Intersputnik offered substantial propaganda value as well. In August, 1968, Premier Kosygin told delegates to a Vienna space conference, "With the aid of both radio and TV transmissions via communications satellites, it becomes possible to influence the culture of the developing countries by advanced countries."

Whatever uses future communications satellites will be put to, both the Communist and Free-World countries know there is new strength to the voices in the sky.

Two Soviet satellites, Cosmos 144 and Cosmos 156, both in polar orbits, pioneered Russia's efforts to link whole world in global satellite network called Intersputnik.

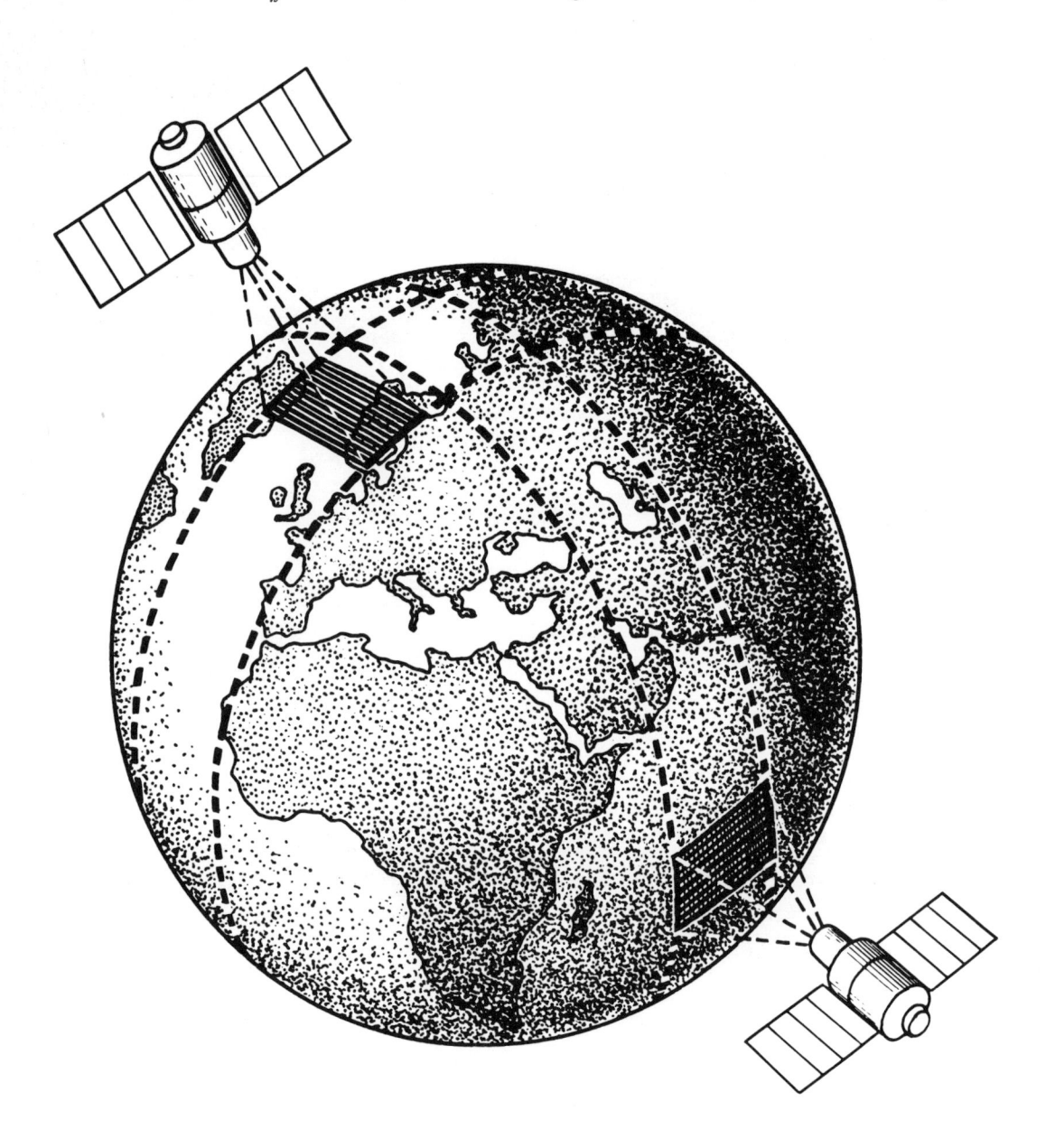

Every satellite in orbit today is watched closely in big Battle Staff Position of North American Air Defense Command (NORAD), deep inside a mountain at Colorado Springs, Colorado. Combat Operation Center officers maintain contact with global operations via Defense Satellite Communications System (DSCS), could immediately alert Pentagon if enemy attack were ever launched against North America.

MILITARY SATELLITES

ALTHOUGH PROJECT SCORE may be considered as this country's first successful "military" satellite, as a product of the Pentagon's Advanced Research Projects Agency in December of 1958, another ARPA project was the first attempt to put communications satellites to military use.

This ARPA project was a study of a narrow-band, non-oriented satellite in a 24-hour orbit over the poles, instead of following the equator. A second, concurrent study involved a synchronous satellite with 60-channel capacity, able to carry both voice and video transmissions.

The Strategic Air Command, responsible for guarding North America against a Russian attack over the North Pole, expressed interest in development of a six-hour polar-orbit repeater satellite to supplement its Distant Early Warning (DEW) Line radar fence.

Eight military satellites are launched simultaneously from huge Titan III-C space booster to join others in forming a necklace of 25 random-orbit satellites, creating world's first global communications net.

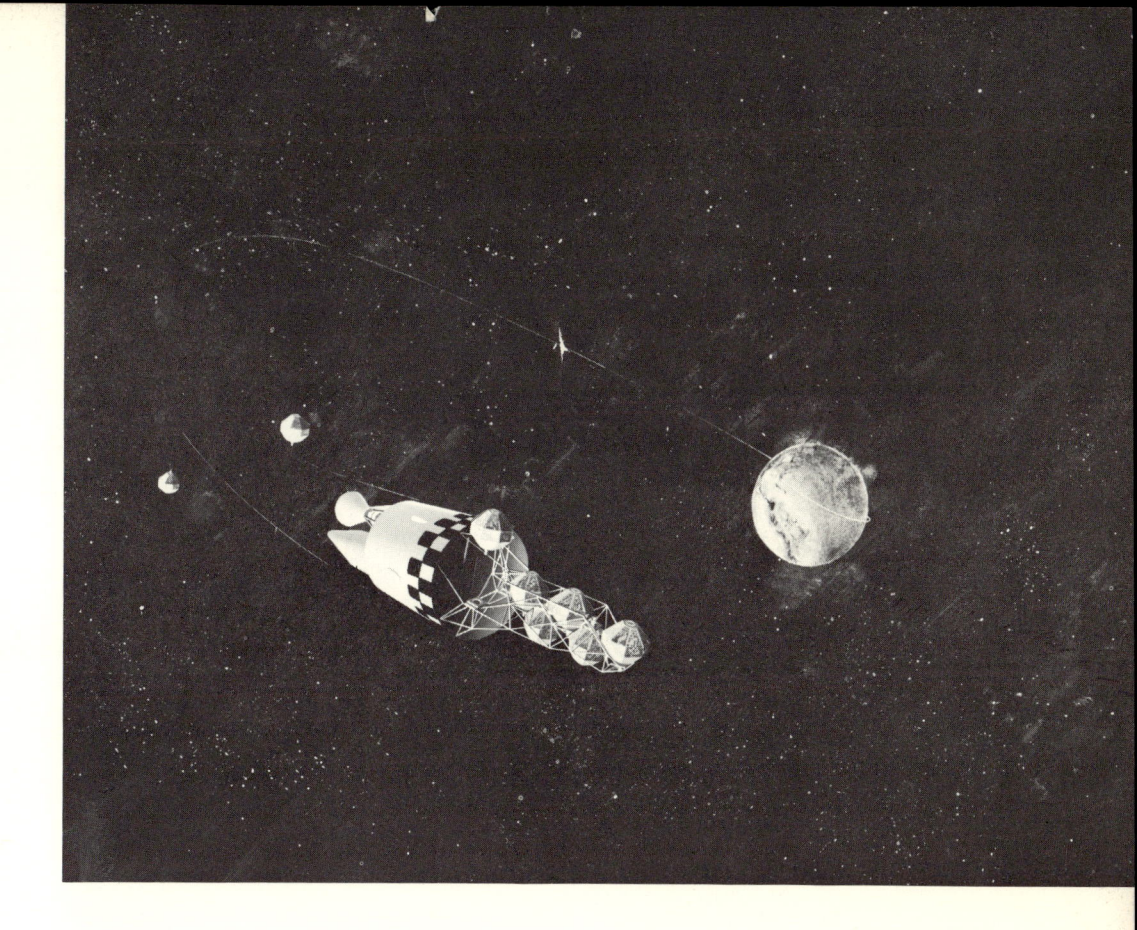

This is how Titan III-C ejects eight communications satellites, like diamonds in the sky, to form military communications net linking Southeast Asia to Washington, D.C., free from natural or manmade interference.

Teaming together, the Air Force and the U. S. Army laid out a development plan which resulted in four unsuccessful projects, called Steer, Tackle, Decree and Advent. Steer was to be SAC's six-hour polar system, operating on UHF (ultrahigh frequencies) with earth-oriented antennas and sun-oriented photoelectric cells for power supply. Problems of complexity and reliability were never resolved.

Tackle was to be a six-hour orbital test bed for Decree, a planned equatorial zone 12-hour satellite, with attitude control, sun-oriented panels and substantial anti-jam protection against enemy radar interference. The launch vehicle was to be the Air Force's Atlas-Centaur.

In 1960 Steer, Tackle and Decree were abandoned by an ARPA directive which established Advent as a synchronous equatorial satellite. Advent looked fine on paper. Highly sophisticated, it included three-axis (pitch, roll and yaw) gyroscopic stabilization, sun-tracking solar panels and other paraphenalia designed to communicate with two ground stations—one at Camp Roberts, California, the other at Fort Dix, New Jersey.

Advent turned out to be a good lesson in over-complication; it seemed that everyone in the Pentagon wanted to hang his ideas on this wishful star in the sky. It simply grew so big that the Atlas-Centaur could never get it off the ground. Advent was scrapped in 1962.

On August 18, 1960, ARPA turned its attention to another concept that did eventually work—Project Courier. This project sought to update Project SCORE, carrying messages both on a delayed and real-time basis. Courier 1A was a 500-pound satellite, sent into a 60-degree inclined orbit by a Thor-Able Star booster. Something went wrong—the rocket exploded.

Two months later, on October 4, Courier 1B did achieve orbit, to become the first active-repeater satellite. During 17 days it carried voice, facsimile and teletype traffic in real-time as well as handling more than 50,000,000 words of "mail bag" courier traffic.

In some respects Courier was the last of an era—the last delayed-repeater, the last Signal Corps satellite launched. It did answer one crucial question—whether long-distance satellite communications were feasible.

Groping for some new, relatively inexpensive means of establishing a global military communications network, the U. S. Air Force, in May, 1963, launched Project West Ford. This was a unique attempt to fill the sky with millions of tiny copper filaments (dipoles) to serve as reflectors for radio messages.

West Ford was a 42-pound package containing 480,000,000 dipoles bound in naphthalene disks, ejected into a 2,300-mile orbit. As the naph-

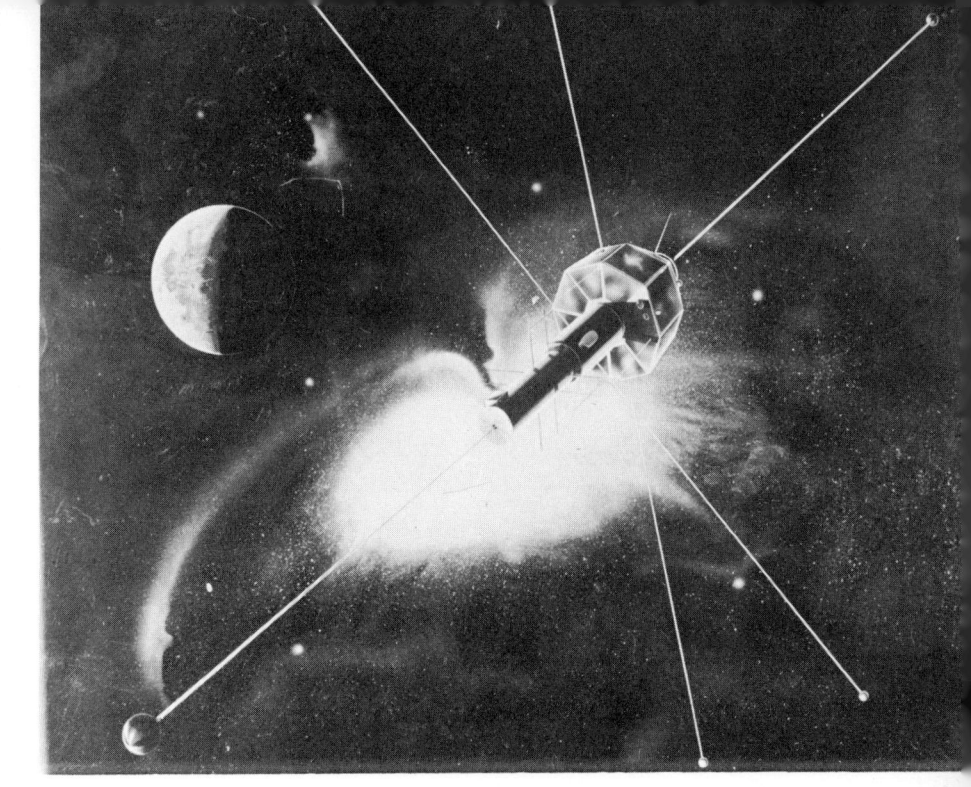

Eight-sided, 430-pound DODGE (Department of Defense Gravity Experiment) satellite contains eight balancing booms, one 150 feet long, plus gyroscopic flywheel for gravity gradient experiment. It carries color TV camera, other electronics gear.

thalene vaporized, the dipoles strung out over a 40,000-mile belt, 20 miles wide and 20 miles thick.

The little wires, only three-fourths inch long and 0.0007 inches in diameter, bunched up and did not work as well as expected, although the USAF claimed the idea did have some merit.

Next, the Pentagon's Defense Communications Agency decided to develop a system of random, medium-altitude satellites to meet the needs of linking Washington, D.C., to distant battlefields in Southeast Asia. In October, 1964, Philco Corporation's Western Development Laboratories Division was given the job of design and development of both satellites and special launchers.

While this system, known as the Initial Defense Communications Satellite Program (IDCSP), was shaping up, another series of experimental satellites was being developed at the Massachusetts Institute of Technology's Lincoln Laboratory, for adaptation to advanced Department of Defense communications satellites.

The first of these was LES-1 (Lincoln Experimental Laboratory-1), a 69-pound polyhedron with 26 surfaces, about two feet across. Launched as a "bonus" payload on a Titan III test vehicle, LES-1 went into the wrong orbit and tumbled end over end. A magnetic spin-axis stability system couldn't be checked out, but another experiment, the first solid-state X-band transmitter aboard a communications satellite, performed well.

LES-2, launched May 6, 1965, aboard the fourth and last Titan IIIA test vehicle, went into orbit and spin-stabilized well. A second experiment aboard, a passive hollow sphere 44 inches in diameter, functioned as a test target for radar and radio calibration. It was called LCS (Lincoln Calibration Sphere).

At last, on June 16, 1966, at one second after 9 A.M., the earth shook at Cape Kennedy's sophisticated ITL (Integrate/Transfer/Launch) Facility as an Air Force Titan IIIC rocket groaned aloft, a 1,402,641-pound monster booster carrying a unique payload of nearly 14 tons.

In this launch the United States initiated its defense communications satellite network by hurling into a near-synchronous orbit, about 21,000 miles above the earth, seven IDCSP (Initial Defense Communications Satellite Program) satellites and one experimental gravity gradient test satellite. The latter was designed to test ways of stabilizing a satellite with long booms which extended in flight, like the balancing pole of a tight-rope walker.

Instead of being ejected all together, seven IDCSP satellites were spewed out one by one, each in a slightly different orbit, to achieve a random pattern able to cover nearly half the earth's surface at one time.

An unprecedented accomplishment, this launch established a relay network of high power (40 watts each) with concentrated signal

First all-solid-state UHF-band satellite, LES-5 (Lincoln Experimental Satellite) features unique antenna system which radiates through slots as spacecraft spins, like early Edison Kinetoscope movie machine.

beams 28 degrees wide. It made possible the field use of small, portable earth terminals (ground stations) like Philco's MASCOT (Mobile Air-Transportable Satellite Communications Terminal). MASCOT can be flown into any trouble zone aboard a C-130 cargo plane or helicopter and assembled by six men in two hours.

The IDCSP network was not yet truly global, however. A total of 24 random orbiting satellites was necessary to achieve its ultimate capacity. Hence, a second launch of eight IDCSP satellites was attempted August 26, 1966. Due to a malfunction in the launcher, they failed to orbit.

The following January 18, Titan IIIC Launch Vehicle 13 rose from Cape Kennedy, hurtled through three burns and two orbital plane changes. Then, one by one, like stripping peas from a pod, another eight IDCSP communications satellites were shot off into 21,000-mile random orbits.

These eight satellites joined the original seven IDCSPs, which already had proven their ruggedness by surviving 53 separate solar eclipses, as they flew in and out of the earth's shadow into the deadly cold of space during the vernal equinox.

Three more IDCSPs went into orbit July 1, 1967, bringing the total to 18 and making the Initial Defense Satellite Communications System operational in the Pacific area, thus providing a space "hot line" between Vietnam and the Pentagon.

Aboard the same Titan IIIC on that launch were three extra experimental satellites called DATS-1, DODGE and LES-5. DATS-1 (Despun Antenna Test Satellite-1) resembled the IDCSP but carried an electronically despun antenna. DODGE (Department of Defense Gravity Experiment) was an eight-sided aluminum shell with a truncated pyramid on top, covered with solar cells and carrying ten gravity-gradient booms. LES-5 included among its experiments a magnetic torquing device, designed to keep it aligned with the earth's polar axis and thus perpendicular to the equatorial plane. It also featured a unique antenna system that radiated messages from the inside through slots, much like Edison's primitive kinetoscope, in which moving pictures appeared on a strip of paper inside a revolving container.

One interesting use of the new IDCSP network was to transmit reconnaissance photographs from Vietnam to the Pentagon, where they were reproduced with laser scanners, giving them a quality equal to the originals.

On June 13, 1968, the Air Force finally completed the world's first global communications satellite system by orbiting eight more IDCSPs into 21,000-mile orbits. They were planned to replenish the 18 already in orbit, but so well did the others function that all 24 worked perfectly at the same time (a twenty-fifth failed).

Using a super-high-frequency X-band for signal transmission, the IDCSP network proved capable of bringing televised pictures of front-line battle scenes into the big War Room of the Pentagon, though other traffic demands held higher priority.

The burgeoning demands of military communications traffic led the Defense Department in 1968 to lease 45 commercial circuits from Intelsat as an interim measure until Phase II of the Defense Satellite Communications System (DSCS) could be built. In one experiment, the U. S. Army Satellite Communications (SATCOM) Agency "double-hopped" an important message from Fort Monmouth, New Jersey, to Asmara, Ethopia. The message went from Fort Monmouth to Camp Roberts, California, by land line; via Syncom III over the Pacific to a Saigon portable terminal; thence back to Syncom II over the Indian Ocean to Asmara.

The advantages of a synchronous orbit system so outweighed the interim benefits of the IDCSP random-orbit network that in late 1968, the Phase II DSCS was being considered by the Office of the Secretary of Defense, as a system of six synchronous satellites. Planned for use in 1971, this network was to employ Philco-Ford satellites able to provide several hundred more channels than IDCSP. Earth-coverage antennas will focus the satellite's radiating power toward earth. Steerable narrow-beam antennas also will spotlight selected areas of earth for still further power concentration, facilitating the use of small portable ground stations in the field.

This new strategic satellite communications system will be comparable to the now-building Intelsat IV commercial network, whose satellites will have a capacity of 6,000 channels. They also will be similar to the IDCSP-A Philco-Ford satellites, built for the United Kingdom for replacement of the British Skynet system, and for the North Atlantic Treaty Organization's (NATO's) North Atlantic Council.

The free world's largest experimental communications satellite, designed to provide tactical communications between army units in the field, ships at sea and aircraft aloft, is the breathtaking finale of the Scientific Sixties decade. Built by Hughes Aircraft Company, it stands as high as a two-story house, weighs 1,600 pounds and can handle up to 10,000 two-way telephone channels, sufficient to link U. S. military commands throughout the entire world.

Dubbed TacSatCom 1, this giant of the communications Space Age was built for launch and testing in early 1969 with an operational date of

RADIATED ENERGY BEAM

ELECTRONICALLY DE-SPUN ANTENNA

SATELLITE SPIN

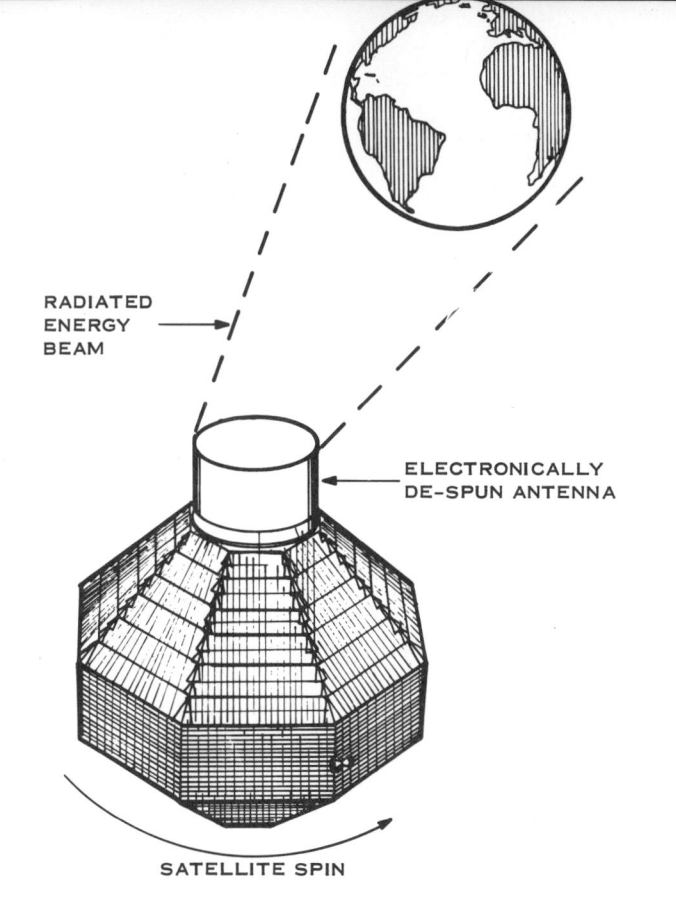

Military satellites use electrically despun antennas to focus transmission beam on earth as satellite continues to spin. Rate of despinning exactly equals spin rate to hold beam steady. Department of Defense Gravity Gradient Experiment (DODGE) satellite undergoes sunlight tests at Johns Hopkins University prior to launch from Cape Kennedy.

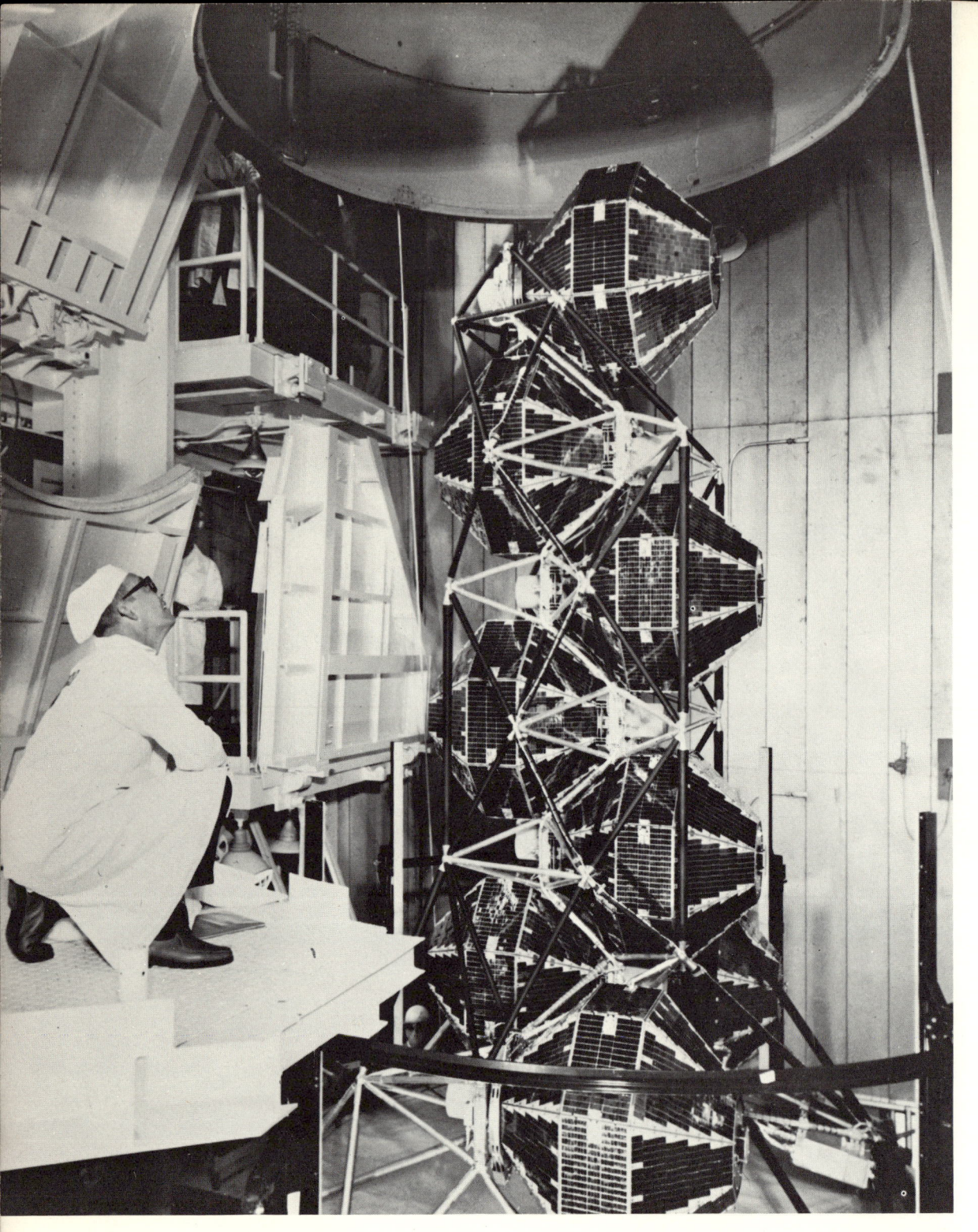

Military IDCSP (Initial Defense Communications Satellite Program) satellites (8 —count 'em!) are carefully packed in spring-loaded dispenser at Philco-Ford's Space and Re-entry Systems Division in Palo Alto, California, which maintains the world's first communications satellite assembly line.

Phase II U.S. military satellite system for 1971 will use satellites like this IDCSP-A, built by Philco-Ford for United Kingdom's Skynet system. Phase II setup will consist of six synchronous satellites to upgrade global military network.

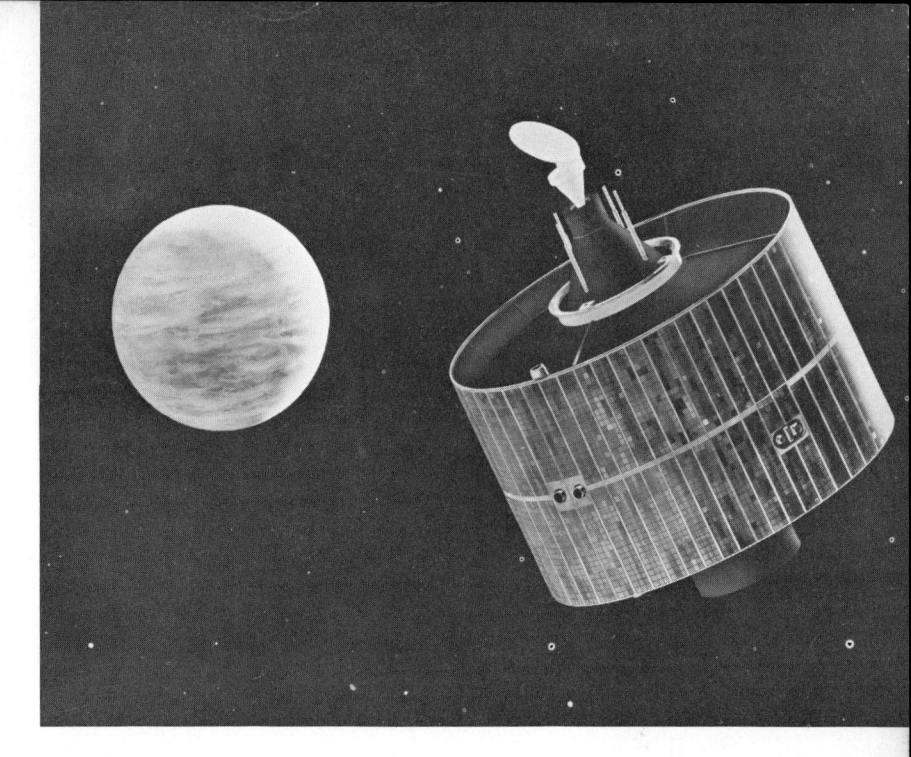

1972. It employs two frequency bands—ultrahigh frequency (UHF) from 225-400 megacycles, the standard military band for air-ground work, and a super-high frequency section of the X-band assigned to military satellite work.

Because of its high power and multiple-access capability, TacSatCom 1 will make possible small, three-foot dish antenna receivers that can be transported by three men and quickly assembled anywhere on earth. Its arrays of antennas, beryllium tubes with dual aluminum helical windings, were designed to be the largest ever orbited.

In the 22 years since the U. S. Signal Corps first bounced radar signals off the moon and back to earth, military space communications have come a long way. By the year 2,000, who knows what space communications—military and civilian—will be like?

Without question there will be worldwide direct dial picture-phones... worldwide color television... face-to-face conference hookups between leaders of industry and government everywhere. And, hopefully, space communications will help us to achieve world peace through better understanding of each other's national problems.

Thundering tailfire of mighty Titan III-C rocket booster lifts futuristic TacSatCom, the world's largest communications satellite, into synchronous orbit in 1969 to open new era of military space communications.

World's biggest communications satellite! Hughes built this full-scale mockup of TacSatCom 1 (Tactical Satellite Communications-1) for testing prior to early 1969 launch. When operational in 1972 TacSatCom, big as a two-story house, will have 10,000 channels reaching into the superhigh X-band radio frequencies.

CHRONOLOGY

Sept. 25, 1956: Transatlantic telephone cable service opened.
Oct. 4, 1957: Soviets launch Sputnik I, first satellite.
Dec. 18, 1958: Project SCORE launched.
Aug. 12, 1960: Echo I, passive satellite, launched.
Aug. 18, 1960: Courier 1A, first active repeater satellite, launched.
Oct. 4, 1960: Courier 1B launched.
July 24, 1961: President John F. Kennedy commits U.S. to build global satellite system.
Dec. 12, 1961: OSCAR I, first "ham" satellite, launched.
July 9, 1962: Megaton nuclear bomb exploded 250 miles over Johnston Island affects Van Allen Radiation Belt.
July 10, 1962: Nuclear bomb radiation encountered by Telstar on first orbit. Telstar "dies" of radiation on Feb. 21, 1963.
Aug. 31, 1962: Communications Satellite Act signed by President Kennedy.
Dec. 13, 1962: Relay 1 launched.
Feb. 1, 1963: Communications Satellite Corp. (Comsat) incorporated.
Feb. 14, 1963: Syncom 1, first synchronous satellite, launched.
May 7, 1963: Telstar II launched.
May 9, 1963: USAF's Project West Ford launched.
July 26, 1963: Syncom 2 launched.
Nov. 22, 1963: First live TV transmission across Pacific.
Jan. 21, 1964: Relay II launched.
Jan. 25 1964: Echo II launched.
Aug. 19, 1964: Syncom 3 launched.
Aug. 20, 1964: Intelsat Consortium created.

Feb. 11, 1965: LES-1 launched.
Apr. 4, 1965: Early Bird (Intelsat 1) launched.
Apr. 23, 1965: Molniya 1A launched.
June 28, 1965: Early Bird begins commercial service.
Oct. 13, 1965: Molniya 1B launched.
Apr. 25, 1966: Molniya 1C launched.
June 16, 1966: IDCSP 1-7, gravity gradient test satellite launched.
Oct. 20, 1966: Molniya 1D launched.
Dec. 6, 1966: ATS-1 launched.
Jan. 11, 1967: Intelsat II (Pacific 1) launched.
Jan. 18, 1967: IDCSP 8-15 launched.
Mar. 22, 1967: Intelsat II (Atlantic 2) launched.
Apr. 5, 1967: ATS-2 launched.
May 24, 1967: Molniya 1E launched.
July 1, 1967: IDCSP 16-18, Dats 1, Dodge, LES-5 launched.
Aug. 14, 1967: President Lyndon B. Johnson appoints task force to report on U.S. communications policy.
Sept. 27, 1967: Intelsat II (Pacific 2) launched.
Oct. 3, 1967: Molniya 1F launched.
Oct. 22, 1967: Molniya 1G launched.
Nov. 7, 1967: Soviet Orbita TV network opens.
Nov. 5, 1967: ATS-3 launched.
June 13, 1968: IDCSPs 19-26 launched.
Sept. 18, 1968: Intelsat III (Atlantic 1) fails to orbit.
Oct. 4, 1968: Intelsat IV ordered by Intelsat Consortium.
Oct. 7, 1968: Molniya 1H launched.

GLOSSARY

ACTIVE (REPEATER) SATELLITE—One which receives, amplifies and retransmits signals from ground stations.

APOGEE—The point in a satellite's orbit furthest from the center of the earth.

COMSAT—Communications Satellite Corporation.

COURIER SATELLITE—One which records messages on tape for later rebroadcast.

DATS—Despun Antenna Test Satellite.

DELAYED REPEATER SATELLITE—One which serves as a courier, recording messages for delayed rebroadcast.

DESPUN ANTENNA—An electronically or mechanically driven antenna system which focuses a broadcast beam on earth by spinning opposite to the satellite's stabilizing spin, at the same rate.

DIPOLE—A tiny copper wire filament, as used in the West Ford Project.

DODGE—Department of Defense Gravity Experiment satellite.

ELLIPTICAL ORBIT—An egg-shaped orbit in which a satellite swings far out to apogee and then back close to perigee.

GROUND STATION—An earth-based transmitting and receiving station.

HF—High Frequency radio band from 3 to 30 megacycles.

ICBM—Intercontinental ballistic missile.

ILLUMINATION—Amount of earth-coverage by radio waves from a communications satellite.

INTELSAT—International Telecommunications Satellite Consortium.

IONOSPHERE—An atmospheric layer of free electrically-charged particles capable of reflecting radio waves.

LASER—Light Amplification by Stimulated Emission of Radiation.

LINE OF SIGHT—An unobstructed line from transmitter to receiver.

MASCOT—Mobile Air-transportable Satellite Communications Terminal.

MASER—Microwave Amplification by Stimulated Emission of Radiation.

MEGACYCLES—One million cycles.

MEGATON—An explosive force equivalent to 1,000,000 tons of TNT.

MICROWAVES—Electromagnetic waves between 100 centimeters and one centimeter in wavelength.

MISSILE—A rocket carrying a warhead.

MOLNIYA—A Soviet satellite whose name means "lightning," capable of carrying news "flashes."

MULTIPLE ACCESS—A satellite relay technique in which several ground stations can use the same channels at once.

ORBIT—The path of one satellite revolving about another body.

ORBITAL INCLINATION—The path of a satellite orbit in relation to the equator, measured in degrees from zero to 180 at true north.
PASSIVE SATELLITE—One which simply reflects microwave signals from one earth station to another.
PERIGEE—The low point in an orbit.
PHASED ARRAY ANTENNA—One which automatically despins a satellite's stability spin at the same rpm.
PHASED ORBIT—One in which communications satellites are spaced so that one rises above the horizon as another sets.
PICTURE-PHONE—A Bell Telephone-developed instrument combining telephone and television.
RANDOM ORBIT—An orbit in which satellites move haphazardly.
REAL-TIME—Instantaneous broadcast or relay of a message.
ROCKET—A space vehicle powered by rearward reacting combustion gases, used to boost spacecraft into various orbits.
SHORTWAVE—A radio wave of 60-meter wavelength or less.
SOLAR CELL—A photoelectric cell capable of converting solar energy into electricity to power spacecraft.
SPACE STATION—An artificial satellite designed for a fixed earth orbit.
SPIN STABILIZATION—A gyroscopic stability system in which a whole satellite revolves to maintain equilibrium.
SYNCHRONOUS SATELLITE—One which appears to be motionless above an equatorial observer, by revolving in an approximate 22,300-mile orbit at the same angular rate as the earth.
TELEMETER—To transmit measurement of a quantity electronically.
TRACK—To visually or electronically follow a satellite across the sky.
TRANSPONDER—A device which transmits one electronic signal on receiving another.
TRAVELING WAVE TUBE—A broad-band amplifier of microwaves, the only vacuum tube used today in communications satellites.
TRIAXIALITY GRAVITY TROUGH—An equatorial region where a synchronous satellite will come to rest by "sliding downhill" into equilibrium of gravity forces from the earth's egg-shaped equatorial bulge. One trough is at 74 degrees east longitude, near India, the other at 108 degrees west longitude, near South America.
UHF—Ultrahigh-frequency radio band from 300 to 3,000 megacycles.
VAN ALLEN BELT—A belt of intense ionizing radiation surrounding the earth in the outer atmosphere.
X BAND—A region of the superhigh-frequency radio band lying between 5,000 and 10,900 megacycles.

INDEX

ABC, 54
Active satellite, 11
Advent, 66
Apollo Project, 50; *ill.,* 15
ARPA, 63
Atlantic II, 54
Atlas missile orbited, 21
Atlas-Agena D booster, 39
ATS-1, 39; *ill.,* 38, 40
ATS-2, 42
ATS-3, 42; *ill.,* 41
A.T.&T., 29, 44

Bell Telephone Laboratory, 30
Broad-band transmission, 24

Cape Canaveral (Kennedy), 19, 21, 30, 38, 51, 68
Charyk, Dr. Joseph V., 47
Clarke, Arthur C., 16, 54
Communications Satellite Act of 1962, 47; *ill.,* 44
Comsat Corporation, 47, 51
Couriers, 22, 28, 66

DATS-1, 69
Decree, 66
Defense Communications Agency, 67
Delayed-repeater satellite, 22
Diana Project, 16, 17
DODGE, 69; *ill.,* 67, 71
Domestic satellites, 13, 54, 60, 61; *ill.,* 13, 56
DSCS, 70

Early Bird, 49, 51; *ill.,* 45
Echo 1, 25; *ill.,* 24, 25
Echo 2, 26
Elliptical orbit, 12; *ill.,* 11
Eurosat, 61
Explorer 1, 21

Field, Cyrus, 14
Ford Foundation, 54

Gravity trough, 38

Ground stations, 29, 33, 60; *ill.,* 14, 46, 48
Gyrostat, 54; *ill.,* 43

Hudspeth, Thomas, 36; *ill.,* 36
Hughes Aircraft Company, 35-37, 39, 54, 70

IDCSP, 67-69; *ill.,* 64, 65, 72, 73
Intelsat Consortium, 16, 47-48
Intelsat II, 49-50; *ill.,* 47
Intelsat III, 51, 55; *ill.,* 48, 52
Intelsat IV, 51, 53, 70; *ill.,* 50
Intersputnik, 60, 62; *ill.,* 62
Ionosphere, 10

Laser, 54
LES satellites, 28, 67-69; *ill.,* 68
Lincoln Laboratory, 67

MASCOT, 69
Maser, 29
Microwaves, 10; *ill.,* 10
Molniyas, 12, 59-60; *ill.,* 58, 59, 61

Nuclear power; *ill.,* 50

Orbita domestic system, 60; *ill.,* 57
OSCAR Project, 28; *ill.,* 26

Pacific 1, 50
Pacific 2, 50
Passive satellite, 11
Phased orbital system, 13
Philco-Ford, 67
Picture-phones, 54; *ill.,* 56

RAND, 17
Random orbit, 12
Relay 1, 33; *ill.,* 31, 32
Relay 2, 34
Rosen, Dr. Harold A., 35; *ill.,* 36
Rostow, Eugene V., 53

SATCOM, 70
Satellite World University, 54

SCORE, 14, 18, 21-23, 63; *ill.,* 20
Shortwaves, 10
Signal Corps, U. S. Army, 16, 73
Skynet, 70
Sputnik 1, 18, 21
Submarine cables, 10, 14-15, 34, 53
Symphonie, 61
Synchronous satellites, 12, 35-55, 60, 70, 73; *ill.,* 17, 18, 39, 53
Syncom 1, 37
Syncom 2, 37, 70
Syncom 3, 38-39, 70; *ill.,* 35, 37

Tackle, 66
TacSatCom 1, 73; *ill.,* 75
Telstar 1, 29-30; *ill.,* 27, 30
Telstar 2, 33
Titan III-C booster, 28, 68-69; *ill.,* 64, 65, 74
TRW Systems, 51

Van Allen Belt, 32-33
Vanguard 1, 21

West Ford Project, 66

X band 67, 70

PICTURE CREDITS

ARINC
    40 (top)

Atomics International
    50 (top)

Comsat Corp.
    9, 10, 11, 13, 14, 15, 17, 18, 27, 30, 31, 37, 42, 44, 45 (bottom), 46, 55, 56 (bottom)

Douglas Aircraft Co.
    24, 35

General Dynamics/Astronautics
    20

Hughes Aircraft Co.
    36, 38, 39, 41, 43, 45 (top), 47, 48 (bottom), 50 (bottom), 75

Johns Hopkins University
    71 (bottom)

NASA
    25, 32, 40 (bottom), 56 (top)

NORAD
    63

Philco-Ford Co.
    72

TASS
    58, 59, 61, 62

TRW Systems
    26, 48 (top), 52, 67, 68

USAF
    71 (top), 73, 74

DATE DUE

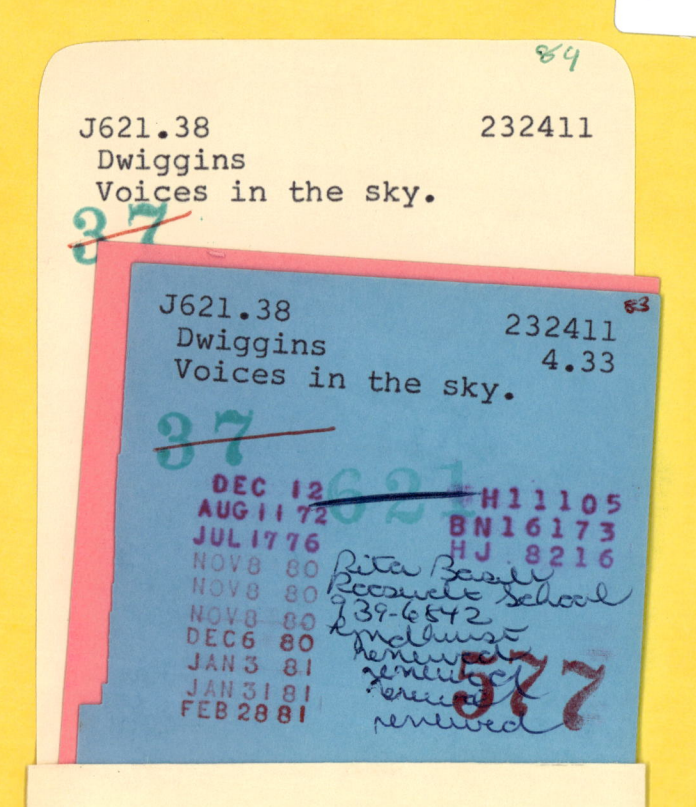

3 9123 00152796 4
HACKENSACK-JOHNSON LIBRARY

J621.38   232411
 Dwiggins
 Voices in the sky.

J621.38   232411
 Dwiggins   4.33
 Voices in the sky.

DEC 12   H 11105
AUG 11 72   BN 16173
JUL 17 76   HJ 8216
NOV 8 80
NOV 8 80
NOV 8 80
DEC 6 80
JAN 3 81
JAN 31 81
FEB 28 81

Johnson Free Public Library
Hackensack, New Jersey